Nuclear High-Altitude Electromagnetic Pulse: A Mortal Threat to the U.S. Power Grid and U.S. Nuclear Power Plants

Steven Starr

Table of Contents

Preface

This book describes the effects of nuclear weapons that produce a maximum High-altitude Electromagnetic Pulse (HEMP) E1 incident energy of 50,000 volts per meter (50 kV/m) – about one-quarter to one-half of the incident energy fields produced by the "Super-EMP" weapons described in Russian[1] and Chinese[2] military sources. Russian open-source military writings claim that Super-EMP weapons generate such powerful fields that even hardened U.S. strategic forces would be vulnerable.[3] If Super-EMP weapons are used in an attack against the U.S., the effects of HEMP could be significantly more severe than those described in this book.

Extreme cold and hot weather conditions would also increase the damage caused by HEMP. Furthermore, the Metatech Corporation, which performed the research upon which much of this book is based upon, used a very conservative approach that may significantly understate the disturbances created by the E3 component of HEMP. Metatech states:

> "... only a 15 second portion of the E3 threat event is
> used in the calculation of equivalent disturbance
> energy. Therefore, the determinations that have been
> made about the geographic extent of power system
> collapse caused by the E3B threat are likely to be best-

---

[1] Vaschenko, A. (November 1, 2006). "Russia: Nuclear Response to America Is Possible Using Super-EMP Factor", "A Nuclear Response To America Is Possible," Zavtra,

[2] Zhao Meng, Da Xinyu, and Zhang Yapu, (May 1, 2014). "Overview of Electromagnetic Pulse Weapons and Protection Techniques Against Them" Winged Missiles (PRC Air Force Engineering University.

[3] Vaschenko, A., Belous, V. (April 13, 2007); "Preparing for the Second Coming of 'Star Wars", *Nezavisimoye Voyennoye Obozreniye* translated in *Russian Considers Missile Defense Response Options* CEP20070413330003.

case projections, and, under less-favorable power grid operating scenarios at the time of attack, the geographic boundaries of collapse could easily be much greater."[4]

In other words, the impacts of HEMP upon the U.S. national power grid and solid-state electronics, which are described in this book, should be considered conservative estimates that are backed up by both real-world experience and extensive testing. Thus, there is a significant probability that the effects of even a single HEMP on the U.S. national power grid and U.S. critical national infrastructure – including U.S. nuclear power plants – will be at least as devastating as those predicted in this book, if not worse.

Steven Starr
Starrst@missouri.edu

---

[4] Gilbert, J., Kappenman, J., Radasky, W. (2010). "The Late-Time (E3) High-Altitude Electromagnetic Pulse (HEMP) and Its Impact on the U.S. Power Grid", Metatech Corporation, Meta R-321. P. 3-3. https://securethegrid.com/wp-content/uploads/2020/01/Metatech-Meta-R-321.pdf.

Introduction: Our Prior Limited Experience with nuclear HEMP

Humanity has had a very limited experience with the High-altitude Electromagnetic Pulse (HEMP) created by a nuclear detonation. Only about 18 nuclear HEMPs have occurred; during the period 1958 through 1962, the U.S. detonated 11 nuclear weapons at altitudes between 16 miles up to hundreds of miles above the Earth.[5] Three of these tests each had an explosive power of more than one megaton (one million tons of TNT explosive power equivalent). The Soviet Union conducted seven tests from September 1961 through November 1962; three of their tests had yields of 300-kilotons (300,000 tons of TNT explosive power equivalent)[6]. These tests were all conducted immediately before the Atmospheric Test Ban Treaty ended above-ground nuclear testing in 1963.

The Soviet tests clearly showed that a HEMP could induce extremely damaging voltages and currents into power transmission and telecommunication lines, which would subsequently damage, disable, or destroy electronic equipment connected to these lines. Today's solid-state electronics are a million times more sensitive to HEMP than were the electronic devices commonly in use in 1962,[7] but unfortunately only the U.S. military has acted to shield its most important equipment from HEMP, while American civil society has remained essentially unprotected from HEMP's catastrophic effects. With more than 12,000 operational and deployed nuclear weapons currently in the arsenals of

---

[5] Hoerlin, H. (October 1976). "United States High-altitude Test Experiences: A Review Emphasizing the Impact on the Environment", Los Alamos Scientific Laboratory. https://sgp.fas.org/othergov/doe/lanl/docs1/00322994.pdf

[6] Emanuelson, J. (July 7, 2019). "Soviet Test 184: The 1962 Soviet Nuclear EMP Tests Over Kazakhstan". https://www.futurescience.com/emp/test184.html

[7] Butt, Y. (January 25, 2010). "The EMP Threat: Fact, Fiction, and Response (Part 1)", The Space Review. https://www.thespacereview.com/article/1549/2

nine nuclear weapon states,[8] it is rather risky to assume that none will ever be used to create a HEMP that – if it occurred today – would almost certainly knock out most or all the U.S. electric power grid for months, while simultaneously disabling, on a regional basis, the solid-state electronics required for the operation of U.S. critical national infrastructure.

The 1962 U.S. Starfish Prime nuclear test detonated a 1.4 megaton nuclear weapon at an altitude of about 249 miles (400 km) over Johnston Island in the North Pacific Ocean.[9] Some measurements of HEMP were made, but because of the limited understanding of HEMP, the few measurements taken provided only the initial evidence that later led to the development of an understanding of the various components of HEMP.[10] The Starfish Prime HEMP occurred about 900 miles (560 km) away from Honolulu and reportedly knocked out about 300 traffic lights and a microwave telecom system.[11] A later study indicated that if the Starfish test had been conducted over central North America, where the Earth's magnetic field is more intense, the destructive effects of this HEMP would likely have been considerably worse.[12]

---

[8] Krsitensen, H. Korda, M., Reynolds, E. (2023). "Status of World Nuclear Forces", Federation of American Scientists. https://fas.org/issues/nuclear-weapons/status-world-nuclear-forces/

[9] Felton, J. (July 12, 2022). "60 Years Ago, The US Exploded a Nuclear Bomb in Outer Space", IFL Science. https://www.iflscience.com/60-years-ago-the-us-exploded-a-nuclear-bomb-in-outer-space-64400

[10] Savage, E., Gilbert, J., Radasky, W. (2010). "The Early-Time (E1) High-Altitude Electromagnetic Pulse (HEMP) and Its Impact on the U.S. Power Grid". Metatech Corporation, Meta R-320, p. 3-1. https://www.futurescience.com/emp/ferc_Meta-R-320.pdf

[11] Seguine, Howard (17 February 1995). "US-Russian meeting – HEMP effects on national power grid & telecommunications". http://ece-research.unm.edu/summa/notes/SDAN/0031.pdf

[12] Longmire, C. (March 1985). "Theoretical Notes, Note 353, EMP on Honolulu from the Starfish Event", Mission Research Corporation. http://ece-research.unm.edu/summa/notes/TheoreticalPDFs/TN353.pdf The U.S. later detonated two more high-altitude nuclear weapons at the same North Pacific

HIGH ALTITUDE ELECTROMAGNETIC PULSE EFFECT (Kazakhstan - October 1962)

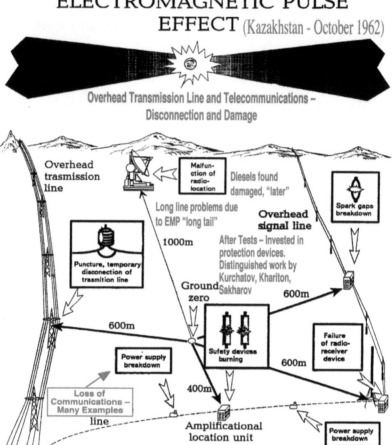

Figure 1: Soviet HEMP test experience, from the effects of the Soviet high altitude test bursts in 1962, as reported by the Russians in June 1994 (From: "Report of the Commission to Assess the Threat to the United States from Electromagnetic Pulse (EMP) Attack," Vol. 1, Executive Report, 2004.)[13]

---

location, and in these cases, the HEMP was reportedly measured successfully, but the results remain classified.

[13] Savage, E., Gilbert, J., Radasky, W. (2010). "The Early-Time (E1) High-Altitude Electromagnetic Pulse (HEMP) and Its Impact on the U.S. Power Grid". Metatech Corporation, Meta R-320, p. 3-6.
https://www.futurescience.com/emp/ferc_Meta-R-320.pdf

The Soviets appeared to have obtained significantly more information about the destructive effects of HEMP with their tests than did the U.S. On October 22, 1962, during the "Project K" test series, the Soviets detonated a 300-kiloton nuclear warhead at an altitude of 180 miles (290 km) over central Kazakhstan. According to a report:

> *"Testing devices were set up to monitor a 350-mile (570-kilometer) section of telephone line in the area the Soviets expected to be affected by the EMP produced by the nuclear detonation. The monitored line was divided into sub-lines of 40 to 80 kilometers (25 to 50 miles) in length. Each sub-line was protected by fuses and overvoltage protectors. The EMP from the 22 October (K-3) nuclear test caused all of the fuses to blow and all of the overvoltage protectors to fire in all of the sub-lines of the 570 km (350 mi) telephone line."*[14]

The E1 component of this Soviet HEMP induced huge currents in a telephone line, which were measured at between 1500 to 3400 amperes. *The induced currents fused all of the 570 km (350 mi) overhead telephone line.*[15] The subsequent E3 component of the HEMP induced massive

---

[14] Greetsai, Vasily N.; Kozlovsky, A.H.; Kuvshinnikov, V.M.; Loborev, V.M.; Parfenov, Y.V.; Tarasov, O.A.; Zdoukhov, L.N. (November 1998). "Response of Long Lines to Nuclear High-Altitude Electromagnetic Pulse (HEMP)". IEEE Transactions on Electromagnetic Compatibility. 40 (4), pp. 348–354. https://ieeexplore.ieee.org/stamp/stamp.jsp?tp=&arnumber=736221
[15] Seguine, Howard (17 February 1995). "US-Russian meeting – HEMP effects on national power grid & telecommunications". http://ece-research.unm.edu/summa/notes/SDAN/0031.pdf Note that at the time of the test,

voltage and currents in buried power lines, which flowed through the lines and caused a fire that destroyed the Karagnada power plant that was about 650 km (400 miles) distant from ground zero. Above ground power line insulators were damaged, short-circuiting the line, and some lines detached from the poles and fell to the ground.[16] A buried communication line more than 600 km (373 miles) away from ground zero was also destroyed, and the E3 component of HEMP shut down 1,000 km (620 miles) of shallow-buried power cables between Astana (then called Aqmola) and Almaty. Antenna systems were affected, and diesel generators failed from the damaging effects of the E1 component of this HEMP.[17].

Under ideal circumstances (using a non-Super EMP weapon), the E1 wave created by a HEMP can today induce peak voltages of 2 million volts into long overhead medium-voltage power lines, which can create a current of 5000[18] to 10,000 amps[19] in these lines. This massive surge of electricity will travel through the grid and, in a few billionths of a second, will disable, damage, or destroy any unshielded modern electronic devices plugged into the grid. This includes damage and destruction of the solid-state circuits *within* all the electronic devices required to run U.S. critical national infrastructure. In regions a few hundred miles

---

there were very few power and telecommunication lines in the area of Kazakhstan where the detonation occurred.

[16] Ibid

[17] Ibid, p. 3-4.

[18] The worst-case HEMP E1 used by the military in MIL-STD-188-125-1 for an E1-induced powerline current of 5,000 amperes. The characteristic impedance for a power line is approximately 400 ohms, thus providing a peak worst-case voltage level of 2 MV. Op. cit. "The Early-Time (E1) High-Altitude Electromagnetic Pulse (HEMP) and Its Impact on the U.S. Power Grid", p. 7-3

[19] Cybersecurity Division of the Cybersecurity and Infrastructure Security Agency, National Coordinating Center for Communications, February 5, 2019. "Electromagnetic Pulse (EMP) Protection and Resilience Guidelines for Critical Infrastructure and Equipment", version 2.2 UNCLASSIFIED, p. 29.

distant from the nuclear detonation, the HEMP E1 can also damage electronics *not* plugged into the grid.

Within the area impacted by E1 – an area covering many tens of thousands of square miles – essentially *all* the solid-state electronics required to operate ground, sea, and air transportation systems, fuel and food distribution systems, water and sanitation systems, telecommunication systems, emergency services, and banking systems would be *simultaneously knocked out*. And the enormous process of repairing and replacing all the electronic devices damaged or destroyed by HEMP E1 would likely have to wait for many months until electric power was again available – *because the E3 component of a single HEMP will bring down and keep down most or all of the U.S. electric power grid*.[20] [21].

Comprehensive studies done by the Metatech Corporation have conclusively demonstrated that the E3A Blast Wave, produced by the HEMP from a single nuclear weapon, will in all likelihood knock out the entire U.S. electric grid.[22] The E3B Heave wave from a detonation over Indiana, Alabama, or Ohio would likely knock out the grid in most of the eastern U.S;[23] a similar E3B wave over Los Angeles would knock out the

---

[20] Gilbert, J., Kappenman, J., Radasky, W. (2010). "The Late-Time (E3) High-Altitude Electromagnetic Pulse (HEMP) and Its Impact on the U.S. Power Grid", Metatech Corporation, Meta R-321. P. 3-2. https://securethegrid.com/wp-content/uploads/2020/01/Metatech-Meta-R-321.pdf
https://www.futurescience.com/emp/ferc_Meta-R-320.pdf
[21] Scientists have found that the E3 wave creates similar effects to those produced by a massive Geomagnetic Disturbance, that is, a Coronal Mass Ejection, or CME, from the sun that strikes the Earth. The largest CME, which occur once every 500 years or so, can also knock out a national electric grid. May, A., Dobrijevic, D. (June 4, 2022). "The Carrington Event: History's Greatest Solar Storm", Space.com. https://www.space.com/the-carrington-event
[22] Op. cit. ""The Late-Time (E3) High-Altitude Electromagnetic Pulse (HEMP) and Its Impact on the U.S. Power Grid", pp. 3-12 through 3-19.
[23] Ibid, pp. 3-5 through 3-7.

grid over the entire U.S. West Coast.[24] The targeting doesn't have to be precise to obtain these disastrous results.

And today, in 2023, if a HEMP should knock out most or all of the grid, entire geographic regions of the U.S. will likely *remain without electric power* for many months, if not for a year or longer. This is primarily because HEMP will damage or destroy a large percentage of the Large Power Transformers (LPTs) required for the long-distance transmission of 90% of U.S. electric power.[25] LPTs are not stockpiled, they are custom designed, and most are made overseas with manufacturing lead times of 18 to 24 months.[26] Unless and until the U.S. acts to protect the LPTs (and their Extra High Voltage Circuit Breakers) from HEMP, the grid will remain totally at risk (this protection would also shield LPTs from the similar effects of a massive Geomagnetic Disturbance, which strikes the Earth every few centuries, see Appendix 4).

Modern society absolutely requires electricity to function; without it, almost nothing we depend upon will work. Imagine the consequences from the complete loss of electric power for a period of many months (or longer) throughout much of the United States. American citizens would instantly find themselves living in the conditions of the 18th century, without running water, lights, phones, functioning toilets and sewage systems, air conditioning and heating. There would be no gasoline available, no food delivered to grocery stores

---

[24] Ibid, p. 5-12.

[25] U.S. Department of Energy, Office of Electricity. "Addressing Security and Reliability Concerns of Large Power Transformers". Retrieved June 1, 2023, from https://www.energy.gov/oe/addressing-security-and-reliability-concerns-large-power-transformers

[26] Distributech International, Powergrid International, Dec 21, 2022, "Inaction on electric transformer crisis adds reliability concerns, APPA warns". https://www.power-grid.com/td/inaction-on-electric-transformer-crisis-adds-to-reliability-concerns-appa-warns/#gref

or restaurants, no refrigeration, no forms of transportation, no access to bank accounts or medical services. A 2017 Congressional Commission to Assess the Threat to the United States from Electromagnetic Pulse Attack stated, "An extended blackout today could result in the death of a large fraction of the American people through the effects of societal collapse, disease, and starvation".[27]

The E1 component of HEMP, which occurs at the speed of light, will also create extreme voltages and currents that can disable or wreck the solid-state components within the Emergency Power Systems and the active Emergency Core Cooling Systems at U.S. nuclear power plants. The failure of these systems, following the emergency shutdown of the nuclear reactors (triggered by the loss of offsite electrical power, when HEMP causes the electric power grid to go down), would likely lead to *the simultaneous meltdown of dozens of nuclear reactors* at the plants in the areas severely affected by the HEMP E1 pulse.

Spent fuel pools are adjacent to each nuclear reactor; they contain highly radioactive used uranium fuel rods that have been removed from the reactor. These pools contain some of the highest concentrations of radioactivity on the planet.[28] Each pool typically contains 4 to 5 times more long-lived radioactive fission products than are found in the reactor core,[29] and the integrity of these pools would be at great risk if the reactor next to them melts down and/or there is a long-term loss of off-site

---

[27] Commission to Assess the Threat to the United States from Electromagnetic Pulse Attack. (July 2017). "Assessing the Threat from Electromagnetic Pulse (EMP)Volume I: Executive Report", p. 4.
https://apps.dtic.mil/sti/pdfs/AD1051492.pdf
[28] Alvarez, R. (May 2011). "Spent Nuclear Fuel Pools in the US: Reducing the Deadly Risks of Storage", Institute for Policy Studies, Washington D.C., p. 1.
https://www.nrc.gov/docs/ML1209/ML120970249.pdf
[29] Alvarez, R. (Winter 2012). "Improving Spent-Fuel Storage at Nuclear Reactors", Issues in Science and Technology, The National Academies of Sciences Engineering Medicine, p. 80. https://issues.org/alvarez/

electric power. This is because the pools must be constantly cooled, or else heat emitted by the spent fuel will heat the water to the point of boiling and expose the spent fuel to steam or air. This would cause the rods to heat to the point of rupture or ignition, releasing huge amounts of highly radioactive gas and smoke. The sudden catastrophic destruction of dozens of nuclear reactors and spent fuel pools would produce gigantic amounts of radioactive fallout that would cover huge areas in the U.S. and leave them too radioactive to live in.[30]

In other words, a single HEMP that occurred today over the United States, in 2023, would likely create complete chaos leading to societal collapse, as well as possibly turning entire states or regions into uninhabitable radioactive wastelands. And this would also be the case for any nation that has not taken significant steps to protect its critical national infrastructure and national electric power grid from the effects of HEMP (as well as a GMD).[19]

The purpose of this book is to demonstrate that this is indeed our present circumstance, as well as to show that **we can still take the steps required to protect the U.S. power grid and our critical national infrastructure – including our nuclear power plants – from HEMP.** We must find the political will to do so.

---

[30] Although the U.S. Nuclear Regulatory Commission (NRC) maintains that HEMP poses no danger to the plants that it regulates, members of the U.S. Airforce Electromagnetic Defense Task Force have pointed out that the NRC has not conducted testing to prove their position is correct. See Part 2 of this report.

Figure 2: The high-altitude detonation of a 3.8 megaton nuclear warhead, in Operation Teak, in 1958.[31] This was the first recorded HEMP. The photo was taken 860 miles away in Hawaii, far enough away to prevent severe retinal burns in the eyes of observers in Honolulu (military officials had moved the site of the test to a different island, because the nuclear fireball could blind people up to 400 miles away).

---

[31] Federal government of the United States, Public domain, via Wikimedia Commons.
https://upload.wikimedia.org/wikipedia/commons/0/03/Hardtack_I_Teak_002.jp g

PART 1

Effects of Nuclear High-altitude Electromagnetic Pulse (HEMP) on the U.S. Power Grid and Critical National Infrastructure

Abstract

A nuclear weapon detonated in the upper atmosphere will produce a High-altitude Electromagnetic Pulse (HEMP).[32] While no blast, fires, or ionizing radiation will be felt on Earth, a single HEMP will instantly create intense electromagnetic fields that will blanket tens or hundreds of thousands of square miles of the Earth's surface.[33] These fields can induce highly destructive transient electric voltages and currents into any electrically conductive material located in the affected regions. A primary concern is that HEMP will induce high voltages and currents into overhead power transmission lines, telecom lines, and cables, which will subsequently damage or destroy a significant portion of any unshielded electronic equipment connected to these lines.

The destructive effects from a single HEMP could knock out much or all of the U.S. national electric grid and in the process, damage or destroy many, if not most of the Large Power Transformers and Extra-High Voltage Circuit Breakers that are required for the long-distance transmission of electrical power. This damage could prevent electrical power from being restored for months or even a year or longer. HEMP will also render inoperable much of the U.S. critical national

---

[32] The nuclear weapon can be carried by a ballistic missile, a satellite, or a high-altitude balloon.

[33] A HEMP created by a high yield nuclear detonation can cause severe retinal burns in people up to 400 miles (640 km) away from the blast.

infrastructure through the destruction of the solid-state electronics and integrated circuits (microchips, microprocessors, logic circuits) that are found within almost all modern electronic devices.

Summary: Effects of HEMP on the National Power Grid

In a timespan measured in a few billionths of a second, the E1 component of HEMP can induce peak voltages of 2 million volts into long overhead medium-voltage power lines, which can create a current of 5000 to 10,000 amps in these lines.[34] [35] These high voltages and currents will destroy tens of millions of insulators on power distribution lines.[36] The failure of a single insulator on a power distribution line can result in the loss of the whole line.[37]

The subsequent E3 component of HEMP, which occurs a number of seconds after E1, would destroy or disable many or most of the Large Power Transformers (LPTs) and Extra-High Voltage (EHV) Circuit Breakers that are required for long distance transmission of power in the U.S. national electric power transmission network (the "grid").[38] LPTs

---

[34] The worst-case HEMP E1 used by the military in MIL-STD-188-125-1 for an E1-induced powerline current of 5,000 amperes. The characteristic impedance for a power line is approximately 400 ohms, thus providing a peak worst-case voltage level of 2 MV. Op. cit. "The Early-Time (E1) High-Altitude Electromagnetic Pulse (HEMP) and Its Impact on the U.S. Power Grid", p. 7-3.

[35] Cybersecurity Division of the Cybersecurity and Infrastructure Security Agency, National Coordinating Center for Communications, February 5, 2019. "Electromagnetic Pulse (EMP) Protection and Resilience Guidelines for Critical Infrastructure and Equipment", version 2.2 UNCLASSIFIED, p. 29.

[36] Personal correspondence with Dr. William Radasky, January 9, 2022.

[37] Savage, E., Gilbert, J., Radasky, W. (January 2010). "The Early-Time (E1) High-Altitude Electromagnetic Pulse (HEMP) and Its Impact on the U.S. Power Grid", Metatech Corporation, Meta-R-320, p. 7-3. http://www.futurescience.com/emp/ferc_Meta-R-320.pdf

[38] There are about 2,000 LPT's in the U.S. rated at or above 345 kV, see Gilbert, J., Kappenman, J., Radasky, E., Savage, E. (January 2010), "The Late-Time (E3) High-Altitude Electromagnetic Pulse (HEMP) and Its Impact on the U.S. Power

make up less than 3% of transformers in U.S. power substations,[39] but 90% of consumed electric power in the U.S. passes through LPTs.[40]

Scientists have confirmed, by *"all means of measurement"*, that *"the threat potential posed by HEMP exceeds the intended stress limit that the U.S. power network is designed and tested to withstand"*[41] (this is also true of the threat potential posed by an extreme Geomagnetic Disturbance or GMD,[42] which has quite similar effects to those created by the E3 component of HEMP, see Appendix 4). A single HEMP could damage or destroy a majority of LPTs and EHV Circuit Breakers in an entire geographic region.

Thus, one HEMP (or massive GMD) would immediately leave entire regions of the U.S. without electric power – and some regions could remain without power for many months or even a year or longer. This is because (1) it will take a long time to manufacture and replace many millions of insulators on power distribution lines, (2) extensive

---

Grid", Metatech Corporation, Meta-R-321, p. 2-32.
http://www.futurescience.com/emp/ferc_Meta-R-321.pdf

[39] Parfomak, P. (June 17, 2014). "Physical Security of the U.S. Power Grid: High-Voltage Transformer Power Stations:", Congressional Research Service, CRS Report Prepared for Members and Committees of Congress. p. 1.

[40] U.S. Department of Energy, Office of Electricity. "Addressing Security and Reliability Concerns of Large Power Transformers". Retrieved June 1, 2023, from https://www.energy.gov/oe/addressing-security-and-reliability-concerns-large-power-transformers

[41] Gilbert, J., Kappenman, J., Radasky, W. (2010). "The Late-Time (E3) High-Altitude Electromagnetic Pulse (HEMP) and Its Impact on the U.S. Power Grid", Metatech Corporation, Meta R-321. P. 3-2.
https://www.futurescience.com/emp/ferc_Meta-R-321.pdf

[42] A massive Geomagnetic Disturbance, or Coronal Mass Ejection (CME), would have the same general effect as the E3 component of HEMP. It is beyond the scope of this paper to discuss CME although it will receive some mention. For detailed analysis, see Kappenman, J. (January 2010). "Geomagnetic Storms and Their Impacts of the U.S. Power Grid", Metatech Corporation, Prepared for Sandia National Laboratories. https://www.futurescience.com/emp/ferc_Meta-R-319.pdf

damage to the EHV Circuit Breakers could take many months to repair,[43] and (3) LPTs would take many months, or a year or longer to manufacture and replace. LPTs are not stockpiled and typically must be custom designed by specially trained engineers, assembled by experienced technicians, have extremely exacting technical specifications, and require extensive testing.

Prior to 2020, the U.S. had to import 82% of its LPTs.[44] The lead time for LPTs manufactured overseas is currently 12 to 18 months.[45] LPTs weigh between 100 to 400 tons;[46] imported LPTs must be shipped by sea freight (too heavy for air freight), which extends shipping times.[47] Transporting huge LPTs to installation points is time consuming and difficult and may add additional months before they can be put into service. If HEMP destroys many or a majority of the LPTs in the U.S. national power grid, *it will likely take at least a year or longer to restore electric power to entire geographic regions in the U.S.*

---

[43] Op. Cit. "The Late-Time (E3) High-Altitude Electromagnetic Pulse (HEMP) and Its Impact on the U.S. Power Grid", p. 5-7.

[44] Postelwait, J. (July 12, 2022). "Transformative Times: Update on the U.S.S. Transformer Supply Chain", T&D World. https://www.tdworld.com/utility-business/article/21243198/transformative-times-update-on-the-us-transformer-supply-chain

[45] Distributech International, Powergrid International, Dec 21, 2022, "Inaction on electric transformer crisis adds reliability concerns, APPA warns". https://www.power-grid.com/td/inaction-on-electric-transformer-crisis-adds-to-reliability-concerns-appa-warns/#gref

[46] U.S. Department of Energy, Office of Electricity Delivery and Energy Reliability. (April 2014). "Large Power Transformers and the U.S. Electric Grid", p. vi. https://www.energy.gov/sites/prod/files/2014/04/f15/LPTStudyUpdate-040914.pdf

[47] Op. cit. "Transformative Times: Update on the U.S.S. Transformer Supply Chain"

Summary: Effects of HEMP on Critical National Infrastructure

The E1 component of HEMP can also disable, damage, or destroy any unprotected solid-state electronics and integrated circuits *within* the modern electronic equipment that is essential to the operations of critical national infrastructure (Figure 3).[48]

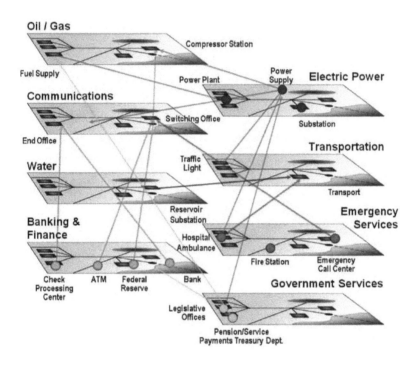

Figure 3: A Conceptual Illustration of the Interconnectedness of Elements Contained Within Each Critical Infrastructure. Some connections are not shown (diagram originally from Sandia National Laboratory).[49]

---

[48] Commercial companies normally cannot afford to place all of their electronics in highly shielded buildings as prescribed by the U.S. military. Radasky, W. (October 31, 2018). "Protecting Industry from HEMP and IEMI", In Compliance Magazine. https://incompliancemag.com/article/protecting-industry-from-hemp-and-iemi/

[49] Critical National Infrastructures. (April 2008). "Report of the Commission to Assess the Threat to the United States from Electromagnetic Pulse (EMP)

Throughout large geographic regions, HEMP would not only stop the delivery of electric power, but it would also wreck the integrated circuits *within* the electronic equipment required to operate:

- ground, sea, rail, and air transportation systems
- fuel and food distribution systems
- water and sanitation systems
- telecommunication systems
- banking systems and electronic financial transactions
- emergency services and governmental services

In addition to the time required to restore electric power, it would also take months to test and replace all the damaged solid-state circuitry and microchips found within the electronic devices required by these systems (assuming replacement parts were available) before most critical national infrastructure in E1-affected regions could resume normal operations.

Without electric power from the grid, U.S. citizens would quickly find themselves without running water, food and refrigeration, lights, functioning toilets and sewage systems, air conditioning and heating, transportation, phones, and communication systems; they would have no access to their bank accounts or medical services. In other words, a single HEMP could now create a complete chaos leading to societal collapse. And this would likely be the case for any nation that has not taken significant steps to protect its national infrastructure from the effects of HEMP.[50]

Attack", Chapter 1, page 12. http://www.empcommission.org/docs/A2473-EMP_Commission-7MB.pdf

[50] Ibid, Chapter 2, page 17. Excerpt: "For most Americans, production of goods and services and most of life's activities stop during a power outage. Not only is it impossible to perform many everyday domestic and workplace tasks, but also people must divert their time to dealing with the consequences of having no electricity. In the extreme, they must focus on survival itself. The situation is not

Summary: We Must Protect the U.S. National Power Grid and Critical National Infrastructure from HEMP

Technology exists that could effectively protect the LPTs from HEMP (and GMD); if installed, it would protect the U.S. power grid from destruction. Likewise, the vulnerable components in U.S. national infrastructure can also be shielded to a significant degree from HEMP (this also holds true for the controls and circuits in the cooling systems and backup power systems at nuclear reactors). There are a number of detailed technical papers that explain how this can be accomplished.[51] [52] [53] [54] [55]

Findings of the 2008 Congressional EMP Commission have led some experts to state that the LPT's and electronic control systems in the national electric grid could be protected from natural and manmade EMP (including HEMP and non-nuclear Intentional Electromagnetic

---

different for the economy at large. No other infrastructure could, by its own collapse alone, create such an outcome."

[51] Kappenman, J. (January 2010), "Low-Frequency Protection Concepts for the Electric Power Grid: Geomagnetically Induced Current (GIC) and E3 HEMP Mitigation", Metatech Corporation, Meta-R-322.
https://www.ferc.gov/sites/default/files/2020-05/ferc_meta-r-322.pdf

[52] The Foundation for Resilient Societies. (September 2020) "Estimating the Cost of Protecting the U.S. Electric Grid from Electromagnetic Pulse.
https://www.resilientsocieties.org/uploads/5/4/0/0/54008795/estimating_the_cost_of_protecting_the_u.s._electric_grid_from_electromagnetic_pulse.pdf

[53] International Electrotechnical Commission. (May 17, 2017). "Electromagnetic compatibility (EMC) - Part 5-10: Installation and mitigation guidelines - Guidance on the protection of facilities against HEMP and IEMI
https://standards.iteh.ai/catalog/standards/iec/b66818ad-403e-47ec-98bb-ba156e7cb367/iec-ts-61000-5-10-2017

[54] Op. cit. Radasky, "Protecting Industry from HEMP and IEMI"

[55] Radasky, W., Savage, E. (Jan 2010). "High-Frequency Protection Concepts for the Electric Power Grid", Metatech Corp, Meta-R-324.
https://www.ferc.gov/sites/default/files/2020-05/ferc_meta-r-324.pdf

Interference devices[56]) for about $2 billion, with implementation, on a non-emergency basis, that would require 3-5 years.[57] Another organization estimated (in 2020) that all national critical infrastructures could be protected for $10 billion to $30 billion dollars.[58] (Note that some critics from the electric utility companies dispute these estimates.[59])

Legislation was drafted in 2013 (the Secure High-Voltage Infrastructure for Electricity From Lethal Damage Act, or the SHIELD Act) and in 2015 (the Critical Infrastructure Protection Act, or CIPA) that would have mandated this protection. However, lobbying by the electric power industry prevented these bills from coming to a vote and killed the legislation.[60] All the various cost estimates to add this protection are in the tens of billions of dollars, which is a small fraction of what the U.S. spends each year on its defense budget.

However, the regulatory agencies for both the electrical and nuclear utilities have to date *resisted* all efforts to install such protective devices, primarily because of the cost involved. No significant steps have yet been taken to install equipment and modifications that would protect the U.S. national electric grid and U.S. critical national infrastructure from HEMP (and this is the situation in many other nations). Thus,

---

[56] Electric Infrastructure Security Council, "IEMI – Intentional Electromagnetic Interference", https://eiscouncil.org/iemi-intentional-electromagnetic-interference/

[57] Secure the Grid Coalition, "EMP: Technology's Worst Nightmare". Retrieved Jan 2022 from https://securethegrid.com/emp-technologys-worst-nightmare/

[58] Op cit. "Estimating the Cost of Protecting the U.S. Electric Grid from Electromagnetic Pulse".

[59] Edison Electric Institute, "Electromagnetic Pulses (EMPs): Myth vs. Facts". Retrieved Jan 07, 2022 from https://inldigitallibrary.inl.gov/sites/STI/STI/INL-EXT-15-35582.pdf

[60] American Leadership and Policy Foundation, (June 2015). "Electromagnetic Pulse and Space Weather and the Strategic Threat to America's Nuclear Power Stations", p. 38. https://www.itstactical.com/wp-content/uploads/2016/08/The-Strategic-Vulnerabilities-of-Nuclear-Plants-to-EMP-and-Solar-Events-ALPF-Final-24-Jan.pdf

American citizens, and many other people around the world, remain very much at risk from the catastrophic effects of HEMP (and GMD).[61]

---

[61] Op. cit. "Low-Frequency Protection Concepts for the Electric Power Grid".

How HEMP Can Destroy the Grid and Modern Electronic Devices

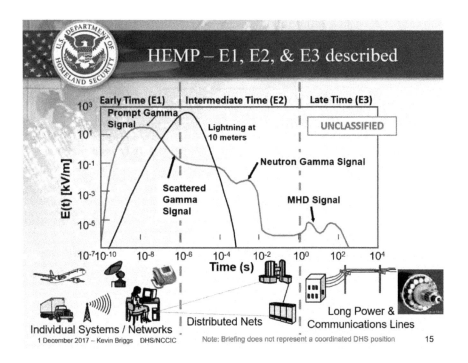

Figure 4: The Various Parts of a Generic HEMP. The left column in the chart illustrates the Electrical energy of E1 in kilovolts per meter (thousands of volts per meter or kV/m).[62] Total Volts per meter produced by Super-EMP weapons may be 2 to 4 times greater in magnitude than those produced by the nuclear weapons used in the calculations utilized.

---

[62] Cybersecurity Division of the Cybersecurity and Infrastructure Security Agency, National Coordinating Center for Communications, February 5, 2019. "Electromagnetic Pulse (EMP) Protection and Resilience Guidelines for Critical Infrastructure and Equipment", version 2.2 UNCLASSIFIED. P. D-3. https://www.cisa.gov/sites/default/files/publications/19_0307_CISA_EMP-Protection-Resilience-Guidelines.pdf

The Three Primary Energy Waves of HEMP: E1, E2, and E3

HEMP is created by a nuclear detonation that occurs above the Earth's lower atmosphere, beginning at an altitude of approximately 30 km (about 19 miles, although this is an approximation).[63] HEMP is a very complex phenomenon, which is made up of three successive energy waves: E1, E2, and E3, with HEMP E1 and E3 considered to be the most dangerous. Power lines, communication lines, and cables act as antennas to conduct the massive voltages and currents induced by HEMP to unshielded electronic equipment. If the connections between the cables and the equipment are unprotected, HEMP pulses could damage or disrupt a significant portion of the electronic devices connected to power or data lines (Figure 4).

The successive electromagnetic fields generated by HEMP can cover vast areas of land, as these energy waves follow a line-of-sight path from the burst point of the nuclear detonation out to the Earth's horizon. In general, the higher the point of detonation, the larger the area covered. However, the distribution of the energy fields created by E1 and E3 (the two most damaging forms of HEMP) are distinctly different and are maximized at different altitudes, so they must be considered on an individual basis.[64]

E1, E2, and E3 are discussed below in the reverse sequence that they occur.

---

[63] Op. Cit. "High-Frequency Protection Concepts for the Electric Power Grid", p. 2-1.

[64] Op. Cit. "The Late-Time (E3) High-Altitude Electromagnetic Pulse (HEMP) and Its Impact on the U.S. Power Grid", p. 2-1

HEMP E3: Two Separate Pulses, E3A Blast Wave and E3B Heave Wave

E3 consists of two distinct waves: E3A followed by E3B. They occur at two distinct times and the electrical fields they create have two distinctively different geographical distributions.[65] Both E3A and E3B pose a grave threat to the Large Power Transformers and their Extra-High Voltage Circuit Breakers, which are required to distribute electricity throughout the U.S. electric power grid (the same holds true for similar unshielded equipment required for other national power grids).

The E3A Blast Wave occurs during a 1 to 10 second interval and consists of a geomagnetic field produced by the expansion of the fireball, which is most likely to effect large power lines. E3A effects are most pronounced at night and its most intense effects are experienced far north of where the detonation occurs. Table 1 provides the latitude and longitude for where the nuclear detonation should occur to maximize the E3A wave in the given location.

Peak fields	Case	Burst Location	
		Lat, deg.min	Long, deg.min
New York	B16A	15.00°N	76.00°W
Chicago	B16B	16.00°N	90.00°W
Dallas/Ft. Worth	B17A	8.30°N	103.00°W
Portland	B15A	21.00°N	132.00°W
Las Vegas	B15B	11.10°N	122.30°W

Table 1: Location of Nuclear Burst to Optimize E3A Blast Wave Effects

---

[65] Op. cit., "The Late-Time (E3) High-Altitude Electromagnetic Pulse (HEMP) and Its Impact on the U.S. Power Grid", p. 1-3.

The higher the detonation and the larger the weapon, the larger are the effects (maximum E3A Blast Wave effects occur at an altitude of about 400 km/259 miles).[66] E3A has a shorter duration than E3B but it produces a more intense geomagnetic field disturbance. *The E3A from a single HEMP detonation can bring down the entire U.S. electric grid.*[67] Figure 5 illustrates the Geomagnetically Induced Current (GIC) from a E3A Blast Wave whose peak electric fields are centered over Chicago. The Metatech study stated, *"Every major state from the East Coast to the west coast states of Washington, Oregon and California, and from Maine to Florida and Texas, accumulated sufficient disturbance energy from this scenario to threaten collapse of the entire U.S. Power Grid."*[68] Figure 6 illustrates the current flows caused by the detonation in Figure 5.

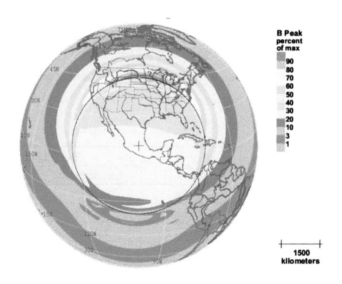

Figure 5: HEMP E3A Blast Wave, the initial
component of HEMP E3, burst height 500 km[69]

---

[66] Ibid, p. 2-14.
[67] Ibid, p. 3-2.
[68] Op. cit., "The Late-Time (E3) High-Altitude Electromagnetic Pulse (HEMP) and Its Impact on the U.S. Power Grid", p. 3-16.
[69] Ibid, p. 2-4

Figure 6: Summary of Geomagnetically Induced Current flows (from HEMP) in U.S. power grid for E3A Blast Wave effects centered over Chicago. **The entire U.S. Power Grid is expected to collapse.**[70]

The E3B Heave Wave follows E3A and occurs during a 10 to 300 second interval. E3B is created by the heated debris ionizing the upper atmosphere while crossing geomagnetic lines that produce currents and magnetic fields beneath it on the surface of the Earth.[71] E3B works by inducing electric currents and magnetic fields into the Earth, which then produce magnetic fields on (or near) the surface of the earth. This will act to induce current into both buried and above ground conductors (especially power lines and phone lines).

In contrast to the E3A Blast Wave, the most damaging effects from E3B Heave Wave occur from a nuclear detonation that occurs at a much lower altitude; its most intense electrical fields are created at a burst height of approximately 150 km.[72] Unlike the E3A Blast Wave, the

---

[70] Ibid.

[71] Ibid, pp. 2-8 and 2-9.

[72] Unlike the E3A Blast Wave, the E3B peak electric field "saturates below a 100-kiloton yield, and larger devices do not produce a higher field, although the

E3B Heave Wave is generally distributed around the point of the nuclear detonation (Figure 7 and Figure 8).

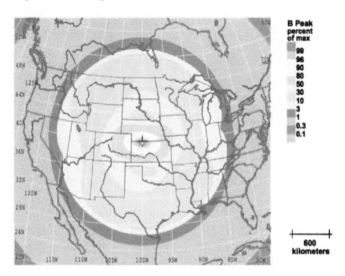

Figure 7: HEMP E3B Heave Wave, height of detonation 130 km (81 miles), explosive power of the nuclear weapon is unspecified.[73]

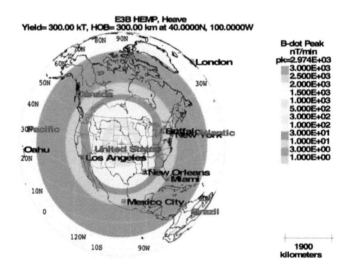

Figure 8: Magnetic Field Peak Contour Pattern from E3B, from a 300-kiloton detonation at a height of 300 km (186 miles)[74]

---

pattern enlarges for larger yields, creating a larger region on the ground where the horizontal electric field is near its peak value." Ibid, p. 2-15.
[73] Ibid, p. 2-12

32

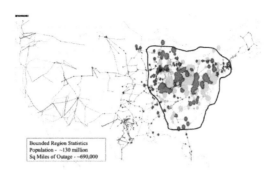

Figure 9: E3B over Columbus, Ohio collapses the grid in circled region[75]

The maximum field strength for E3B is developed in the regions directly below the detonation where the atmosphere is most intensely heated.[76] *The E3B from a single HEMP can bring down the electric grid over an entire geographic region such as the Eastern and Southeastern U.S.* (Figure 9) *or the West Coast of the U.S.* (Figure 10).[77]

Figure 10: E3B over Portland, Oregon collapses the grid in circled region[78]

---

[74] National Coordinating Center for Communications. (Feb 5, 2019). "Electromagnetic Pulse (EMP) Protection and Resilience Guidelines for Critical Infrastructure and Equipment", Version 2.2, National Cybersecurity and Communications Integration Center, Arlington, Virginia, p. 10. https://www.cisa.gov/sites/default/files/publications/19_0307_CISA_EMP-Protection-Resilience-Guidelines.pdf

[75] Op. cit., "The Late-Time (E3) High-Altitude Electromagnetic Pulse (HEMP) and Its Impact on the U.S. Power Grid", p. 3-5.

[76] Ibid, p. 2-11.

[77] Ibid, pp. 3-5 through 3-12.

[78] Ibid, p. 3-11.

Deadly Threat to the U.S. Power Grid from nuclear HEMP E3

The E3 wave is also called Magneto-hydrodynamic or MHD EMP as it arises from the motion of the ionized bomb debris and atmosphere relative to the geomagnetic field.[79] Unlike E1 and E2, which essentially act *above* ground level, E3 will *also* induce powerful current flows *well below ground level* into buried communication and power transmission lines.[80] E3 acts in a very similar manner to the destructive Geomagnetically Induced Current (GIC) produced during a geomagnetic storm, although a nuclear E3 pulse can be significantly more intense than a solar storm induced GMD pulse[81] (see Appendix 4). The effects of E3 are much more pronounced if the detonation occurs during the hours of darkness, during *nighttime* at the minimum of the solar cycle.[82] The calculations and Figures used here are based on detonations that occur at night.

E3 primarily damages high voltage equipment connected to long-distance electric transmission lines, especially High-Speed Circuit Breakers and Large Power Transformers (LPTs) over 100,000 volts (100

---

[79] Op. cit., "The Late-Time (E3) High-Altitude Electromagnetic Pulse (HEMP) and Its Impact on the U.S. Power Grid", p. 2-1.

[80] Op. cit. "The Late-Time (E3) High-Altitude Electromagnetic Pulse (HEMP) and Its Impact on the U.S. Power Grid", p. 2-18. & Emanuelson, J. (July 7, 2019). "Soviet Test 184: The Soviet 1962 EMP Test over Kazakhstan". https://www.futurescience.com/emp/test184.html

[81] "Geomagnetic storm and E3 HEMP environments can develop almost instantaneously over large geographic footprints, which have the ability to essentially blanket the continent with an intense threat environment and have the capability to produce significant collateral damage to critical infrastructures . . . no comprehensive design criteria have ever been considered to check the impact of the geomagnetic storm environment.", Op. Cit. "The Late-Time (E3) High-Altitude Electromagnetic Pulse (HEMP) and Its Impact on the U.S. Power Grid", pp. 2-46, 2-47.

[82] Ibid, p. 2-7.

kV). LPTs are an absolutely essential part of the national electric grid; they are required for the long-distance transmission of electric power.

LPTs convert or "transform" voltage into a required voltage. Generator Step-Up (GSU) transformers, located at power plants, increase voltages prior to long-distance transmission (higher voltage with reduced current acts to reduce power loss in transmission lines); Large Power Step Down transformers, located at the receiving end, act to reduce voltage and increase the current. According to the Energy Department's Office of Electricity, over 90 percent of the electricity consumed in the U.S. passes through LPTs.[83]

Vulnerability of Large Power Transformers (LPTs) and High-Speed Circuit Breakers to HEMP E3

The 345 kV, 500 kV, and 765 kV LPTs that populate the U.S. national electric power grid, if left unshielded, all are extremely susceptible to E3 and GMD (see Appendix 4 for GMD information).[84] Should many or most of these LPTs be put out of operation, much or all of the U.S. national electric grid would be put out of service. Figure 11 illustrates the critical role played by LPTs in the U.S. national electric power grid. The Generator Step-Up and Step-Down transformers that are circled in red are the LPTs at most risk.

[83] Op. cit. "Transformative Times: Update on the U.S. Transformer Supply Chain
[84] Op. cit., "The Late-Time (E3) High-Altitude Electromagnetic Pulse (HEMP) and Its Impact on the U.S. Power Grid", p. 2-32.

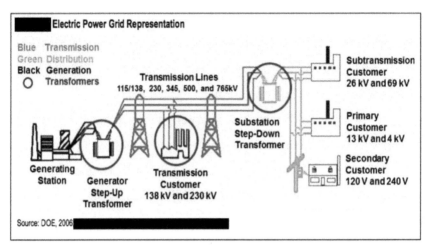

Figure 11: Large Power Transformers (LPTs) circled in red. LPTs are essential for the U.S. national power grid to operate.[85]

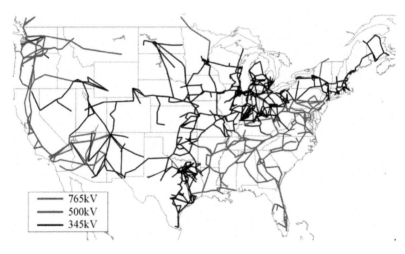

Figure 12: U.S. High-Voltage Transmission Lines[86]

---

[85] U.S.-Canada Power System Outage Task Force. (April 2004). "U.S.-Canada Power System Outage Task Force, Final Report on the August 14, 2003 Blackout in the United States and Canada: Causes and Recommendations", Figure 2.1, p. 5.
https://www.energy.gov/sites/default/files/oeprod/DocumentsandMedia/Blackout Final-Web.pdf
[86] Ibid, p. 2-31.

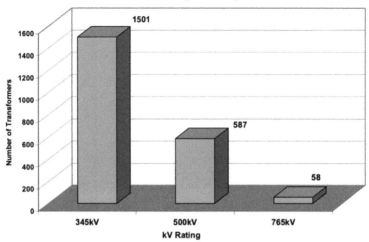

Figure 13: Large Power Transformers (LPTs) in the U.S. national electric grid.[87]

There are approximately 1800 major transmission lines of 345 kV or higher operating voltage, and about 5000 circuit breakers of 345 kV or higher operating voltage across the contiguous United States (Figure 12);[88] most, if not all of these would be knocked out of commission by the combined effects of HEMP E3A. Figure 13 illustrates the number and percentages of LPTs used in the U.S. national electric grid.

The U.S. electrical power grid, which supports all the other critical infrastructures, is already extremely fragile and vulnerable to any EMP attack.[89] The average age of installed LPTs in the United States is

[87] Ibid, p. 2-32.

[88] Op. cit., "The Late-Time (E3) High-Altitude Electromagnetic Pulse (HEMP) and Its Impact on the U.S. Power Grid", p. 4-2.

[89] Radasky, W., Pry, P. (July 6, 2010). "Rebuttal to "The EMP threat: fact, fiction, and response", The Space Review in association with Space News. https://www.thespacereview.com/article/1656/1

about 38 to 40 years, with 70 percent of LPTs being 25 years or older.[90] There are only 8 companies in the U.S. currently manufacturing LPTs[91] and there is only one U.S. company that manufactures the Grain-Oriented Electrical Steel required to make the cores and laminations inside LPTs.[92] A heavily redacted report published in 2020 by the Department of Commerce stated:

> *"Of particular concern is lack of domestic capacity with regard to extra high voltage transformers (those with >345 kV voltage rating) that are vital for long distance electricity transmission. This excessive level of foreign dependence on imported LPT, which are uniquely critical to the U.S. Bulk Power System puts the resiliency of the critical energy infrastructure at risk."[93]*

The current lead time for domestic production of LPTs is 38 months,[94] however, it would probably be impossible to domestically manufacture LPTs if all or most of the U.S. national electric grid was down for months or longer. The lead time for LPTs manufactured

---

[90] U.S. Department of Energy, Office of Electricity Delivery and Energy Reliability. (April 2014). "Large Power Transformers and the U.S. Electric Grid", p. v.
https://www.energy.gov/sites/prod/files/2014/04/f15/LPTStudyUpdate-040914.pdf
[91] Op. cit. "How a transformer shortage threatens the grid"
[92] U.S. Department of Commerce. (October 15, 2020). "The Effect of Imports of Transformers and Transformer Components on the National Security, Final Report", Bureau of Industry and Security, Office of Technology Evaluation, p. 9.
https://www.bis.doc.gov/index.php/documents/section-232-investigations/2790-redacted-goes-report-20210723-ab-redacted/file
[93] Op. cit. "The Effect of Imports of Transformers and Transformer Components on the National Security, Final Report", p. 233.
[94] Op. cit. "Transformative Times: Update on the US.S. Transformer Supply Chain"

overseas is currently 12 to 18 months.[95] 345 to 765 kV LPTs typically weigh from 370,000 to 820,000 pounds (Table 2); the heaviest load a railroad car typically carries is 200,000 pounds.[96] Imported LPTs must be shipped by sea freight (too heavy for air freight), which extends shipping times.[97]

Voltage Rating (Primary-Secondary)	Capability MVA Rating	Approximate Price ($)	Approximate Weight & Dimensions
Transmission Transformer			
Three Phase			
230–115kV	300	$2,000,000	170 tons (340,000 lb) 21ft W–27ft L–25ft H
345–138kV	500	$4,000,000	335 tons (670,000 lb) 45ft W–25ft L–30ft H
765–138kV	750	$7,500,000	410 tons (820,000 lb) 56ft W–40ft L–45ft H
Single Phase			
765–345kV	500	$4,500,000	235 tons (470,000 lb) 40ft W–30ft L–40ft H
Generator Step-Up Transformer			
Three Phase			
115–13.8kV	75	$1,000,000	110 tons (220,000 lb) 16ft W–25ft L–20ft H
345—13.8kV	300	$2,500,000	185 tons (370,000 lb) 21ft W–40ft L–27ft H
Single Phase			
345–22kV	300	$3,000,000	225 tons (450,000 lb) 35ft W–20ft L–30ft H
765–26kV	500	$5,000,000	325 tons (650,000 lb) 33ft W–25ft L–40ft H

Table 2: Large Power Transformers are huge and difficult to transport.[98] Transportation is an important element of the total LPT cost, due to their weight.

[95] Op. cit. "Inaction on electric transformer crisis adds reliability concerns, APPA warns"

[96] U.S. Department of Energy, Infrastructure Security and Energy Restoration Office of Electricity Delivery and Energy Reliability (April 2014) "Large Power Transformers and the U.S. Electric Grid", p. vi. https://www.energy.gov/sites/prod/files/2014/04/f15/LPTStudyUpdate-040914.pdf

[97] Op. cit. "Transformative Times: Update on the U.S.S. Transformer Supply Chain"

[98] Csyani, E. (December 30, 2013). "Large Power Transformer Tailored to Customer's Specifications", Electrical Engineering Portal. https://electrical-engineering-portal.com/an-overview-of-large-power-transformer-lpt

Figure 14: Workers move wires, lights, and poles to transport a 340-ton LPT, causing hours of traffic delay. LPTs can weigh up to 400 tons, four times more than rail transport can handle.[99]

Even if the national electric grid was functional, it would be a logistical nightmare to move many hundreds of replacement LPTs following a HEMP (Figure 14). This might prove to be a nearly impossible task in a situation where the grid had been down for many months.

Extra-High Voltage Circuit Breakers also Destroyed by HEMP E3

A primary task of the Extra-High Voltage (EHV) Circuit Breakers is to interrupt fault currents, which are usually at least several times greater than those normally flowing through the circuit. Unfortunately, the E3 component of HEMP can induce *"extraordinarily high levels of Geomagnetically Induced Current"* into these lines that EHV Circuit Breakers cannot withstand.[100] The Metatech Corporation found that the E3A Blast Wave would put ~1500 to 2000 EHV Circuit

[99] Op. cit. "Large Power Transformers and the U.S. Electric Grid", p. vi
[100] Op. cit., "The Late-Time (E3) High-Altitude Electromagnetic Pulse (HEMP) and Its Impact on the U.S. Power Grid, p. 5-7.

Breakers at-risk, a level that is approximately one-third of the entire U.S. population of circuit breakers[101] (Figure 15).

Figure 15: Location of at-risk EHV Circuit Breakers from for E3A Blast Wave effects centered over Chicago. Metatech calculates ~1500 to 2000 circuit breakers at-risk, a level that is approximately one-third of the entire U.S. population of circuit breakers.[102]

Metatech estimated that it would take months to repair this damage.[103] Current lead times to manufacture EHV Circuit Breakers overseas is about one year minimum (approximately half of the EHV Circuit Breakers are manufactured in Germany in China).[104] Mitsubishi opened a U.S. plant, in 2021 with an 8-month lead time for production.[105] However, domestic manufacture of EHV Circuit Breakers could prove

[101] Ibid, p. 5-17.
[102] Ibid, p. 4-15.
[103] Ibid, p. 5-7.
[104] The Douglas Company. Retrieved May 2023 from https://www.douglascompany.com/tag/electrical-components/
[105] Mitsubishi Power Products, Inc. (April 5, 2021). "MEPPI Introduces 245kV Gas Insulated Switchgear for Utility Transmission Applications. https://meppi.com/news/meppi-introduces-245kv-gas-insulated-switchgear-for-utility-transmission-applications

impossible if the region where the factory is located has lost off-site electrical power from the grid being knocked out by HEMP.

HEMP E3: Summary of effects

Scientists have confirmed, by *"all means of measurement"*, that the threat potential posed by HEMP exceeds the intended stress limit that the U.S. power network is designed and tested to withstand[106] (this is also true for an extreme Geomagnetic Disturbance or GMD,[107] see Appendix 4). Both E3A and E3B will induce large, damaging currents into electric power transmission lines and buried transmission lines.[108] This will cause near-simultaneous, multipoint failures in power system infrastructures and includes the widespread damage and destruction of Large Power Transformers (LPTs)[109] and EHV Circuit Breakers.[110] *A single HEMP would likely damage or destroy a majority of LPTs and EHV Circuit Breakers in large geographic regions within the U.S. electric power grid, leaving tens or hundreds of millions of U.S. citizens without electricity for many months or even a year, due to the time required to replace the LPTs and EHV Circuit Breakers.*

---

[106] Op. cit., "The Late-Time (E3) High-Altitude Electromagnetic Pulse (HEMP) and Its Impact on the U.S. Power Grid", p. 3-2

[107] A massive Geomagnetic Disturbance, or Coronal Mass Ejection (CME), would have the same general effect as the E3 component of HEMP. It is beyond the scope of this paper to discuss CME although it will receive some mention. For detailed analysis, see Kappenman, J. (January 2010). "Geomagnetic Storms and Their Impacts of the U.S. Power Grid", Metatech Corporation, Prepared for Sandia National Laboratories. https://www.futurescience.com/emp/ferc_Meta-R-319.pdf

[108] Ibid, page 2-18

[109] Op. cit., "The Late-Time (E3) High-Altitude Electromagnetic Pulse (HEMP) and Its Impact on the U.S. Power Grid", pp. 2-46 and 2-47. There would be little or no time for meaningful human interventions in such circumstances.
[110]

Preventative Measures to Protect the National Grid from HEMP

Technology exists that could effectively protect the LPTs from both HEMP and GMD; if installed, it would protect the U.S. power grid from destruction. There are a number of detailed technical papers that explain how this can be accomplished.[111] [112] [113] [114] [115] Findings of the 2008 Congressional EMP Commission have led some experts to state that the LPT's and electronic control systems in the national electric grid could be protected from natural and manmade EMP (including HEMP and non-nuclear Intentional Electromagnetic Interference devices[116]) for about $2 billion, with implementation, on a non-emergency basis, that would require 3-5 years.[117] Another organization estimated (in 2020) that all national critical infrastructures could be protected for $10 billion to $30 billion dollars.[118] (Note that some critics from the electric utility

---

[111] Kappenman, J. (January 2010), "Low-Frequency Protection Concepts for the Electric Power Grid: Geomagnetically Induced Current (GIC) and E3 HEMP Mitigation", Metatech Corporation, Meta-R-322. https://www.ferc.gov/sites/default/files/2020-05/ferc_meta-r-322.pdf

[112] The Foundation for Resilient Societies, "Estimating the Cost of Protecting the U.S. Electric Grid from Electromagnetic Pulse, September 2020. https://www.resilientsocieties.org/uploads/5/4/0/0/54008795/estimating_the_cost_of_protecting_the_u.s._electric_grid_from_electromagnetic_pulse.pdf

[113] International Electrotechnical Commission. (17-May-2017). "Electromagnetic compatibility (EMC) - Part 5-10: Installation and mitigation guidelines - Guidance on the protection of facilities against HEMP and IEMI https://standards.iteh.ai/catalog/standards/iec/b66818ad-403e-47ec-98bb-ba156e7cb367/iec-ts-61000-5-10-2017

[114] Op. cit. Radasky, "Protecting Industry from HEMP and IEMI"

[115] Op. cit. "High-Frequency Protection Concepts for the Electric Power Grid"

[116] Electric Infrastructure Security Council, "IEMI – Intentional Electromagnetic Interference", https://eiscouncil.org/iemi-intentional-electromagnetic-interference/

[117] Secure the Grid Coalition, (Jan 12, 2023). "EMP: Technology's Worst Nightmare". https://securethegrid.com/emp-technologys-worst-nightmare/

[118] Op cit. "Estimating the Cost of Protecting the U.S. Electric Grid from Electromagnetic Pulse".

companies dispute these estimates.[119]) Legislation was drafted in 2013 (the Secure High-Voltage Infrastructure for Electricity From Lethal Damage Act, or the SHIELD Act) and in 2015 (the Critical Infrastructure Protection Act, or CIPA) that would have mandated this protection. However, lobbying by the electric power industry prevented these bills from coming to a vote and killed the legislation.[120]

In March 2017, the Assistant Secretary of the Department of Energy instructed the Electric Reliability Organization,[121] and owners of critical electric infrastructure and defense and military installations, to

> ". . . prepare and submit to Congress a plan to establish a Strategic Transformer Reserve for the storage, in strategically located facilities, of spare large power transformers and emergency mobile substations in sufficient numbers to temporarily replace critically damaged large power transformers and substations that are critical electric infrastructure or serve defense and military installations."[122]

---

[119] Edison Electric Institute, (Jan 2016). "Electromagnetic Pulses (EMPs): Myth vs. Facts". https://inldigitallibrary.inl.gov/sites/STI/STI/INL-EXT-15-35582.pdf

[120] American Leadership and Policy Foundation, (June 2015). "Electromagnetic Pulse and Space Weather and the Strategic Threat to America's Nuclear Power Stations", p. 38. https://www.itstactical.com/wp-content/uploads/2016/08/The-Strategic-Vulnerabilities-of-Nuclear-Plants-to-EMP-and-Solar-Events-ALPF-Final-24-Jan.pdf

[121] An organization that has been certified by the Federal Energy Regulatory Commission (FERC) to establish and enforce reliability standards for the U.S. bulk power system.

[122] U.S. Department of Energy. (March 2017). "Strategic Transformer Reserve", Report to Congress. https://www.energy.gov/sites/prod/files/2017/04/f34/Strategic%20Transformer%20Reserve%20Report%20-%20FINAL.pdf

Unfortunately, no Strategic Transformer Reserve has been created, although a new design for a "Flexible Transformer" has been successfully developed by General Electric Renewable Energy's Grid Solutions unit.[123] A unit with variable settings, ranging from 69kV to 161kV, has been built and tested;[124] GE engineers are currently working on designs for the LPTs.

However, the opposition from electric utilities and lack of interest from the Biden administration has currently resulted in no Federal legislation mandating comprehensive action to protect LPTs from HEMP/EMP. This leaves the U.S. national electric grid – and the American public – at extreme risk from HEMP.

HEMP E2: Effects Similar to Those Produced by Lightning

E2 follows E1 and E2 lasts only one or two seconds. E2 is similar to lightning and can inflict a similar level of damaging energy, but it is of less concern than E1 or E3 because most electronic systems have some protection against E2.[125] However, E1 may damage or disable electronic systems including surge protection systems that protect against E2, leaving them vulnerable to the effects of the E2 and E3 waves that follow. The specialized devices and techniques that protect against E1 will help protect against E2.[126]

---

[123] Kellner, T. (October 27, 2021). "Special Power: 'Flexible Transformer' Could Become the Grid's New Superhero", https://www.ge.com/news/reports/special-power-flexible-transformer-could-become-the-grids-new-superhero
[124] Personal communication with John Gilbertson of Cooperative Energy of Hattiesburg, Mississippi Jan 19, 2023.
[125] The fact that E2 will immediately follow E1 may allow E2 to cause damage, because the E1 has damaged or destroyed the devices designed to protect against E2.
[126] National Coordinating Center for Communications. (Feb 5, 2019). "Electromagnetic Pulse (EMP) Protection and Resilience Guidelines for Critical Infrastructure and Equipment", Version 2.2, National

HEMP E1: Overview

E1 is called "Early Time HEMP" and is generated instantaneously at the moment of nuclear detonation. E1 is also called the "prompt gamma signal" because is created by the gamma rays released by the nuclear detonation that travel outward at the speed of light. Those gamma rays, traveling downward from the detonation, begin to strike air molecules at a height of 40 to 20 km (25 to 12 miles) and strip electrons from them. These high energy electrons are also directed downward towards the Earth. The Earth's gravity causes the electrons to spin; this constitutes an electric current that creates a very large and powerful electromagnetic field, which will engulf entire geographic regions in a few billionths of a second[127] after the detonation.[128]

E1 primarily affects above-ground electrical conductors. While E1 can penetrate the Earth, most of E1 is reflected from Earth's surface (reflected E1 also can induce current and voltage). E1 does not affect lines buried 1-2 meters deep.[129] The electric fields generated by E1 are

---

Cybersecurity and Communications Integration Center, Arlington, Virginia, p. 4.
https://www.cisa.gov/sites/default/files/publications/19_0307_CISA_EMP-Protection-Resilience-Guidelines.pdf
https://www.cisa.gov/sites/default/files/publications/19_0307_CISA_EMP-Protection-Resilience-Guidelines.pdf

[127] Interference Technology. (May 5, 2011). "High Power Electromagnetic (HPEM) Threats to the Smart Grid". https://interferencetechnology.com/high-power-electromagnetic-hpem-threats-to-the-smart-grid/

[128] Ibid, pp. 4-1 and 4-2. There is a relatively small "null" area that is not impacted, due to the complexities of how HEMP is formed, see Figure 16.

[129] The least coupling is for buried cables; often a meter or two below ground provides significant protection from E1 HEMP fields. The total driver of the coupling is the incident HEMP E1 pulse plus its reflection off the ground. Savage, Edward, James Gilbert, and William Radasky. (2010). "The Early-Time (E1) High-Altitude Electromagnetic Pulse (HEMP) and Its Impact on the U.S. Power Grid". Metatech Corporation, Meta R-320, p. 5-2. https://www.futurescience.com/emp/ferc_Meta-R-320.pdf

much more severe in intensity than the electric fields caused by natural events, such as lightning. Only special transient protectors are fast enough to protect integrated circuits against the high voltages and currents created by HEMP E1, which occur so quickly that ordinary "surge protection" systems are unable to stop it.[130]

Electronic devices with solid-state circuitry and integrated circuits will be most vulnerable if they are powered up and connected to the grid. Electronic devices that are powered off are likely to be less susceptible, however E1 can induce high voltages and currents into even short lengths of cables or power cords that are attached to the device. In regions where incident E1 levels are high, even devices that are completely unconnected to a power source can still be damaged, disabled, or made inoperable by the voltages and currents induced by E1.

Entire geographic regions subjected to enormous levels of HEMP E1

Figure 16 illustrates the line-of-sight area covered by E1. The strongest E1 pulses are produced by nuclear detonations that occur at altitudes between 40 km and 100 km (25 to 62 miles). It appears that the maximum E1 waves are created at a height of about 75 km (42 miles).[131] The explosive power of the nuclear detonation can range from a few kilotons to tens of megatons, but the maximum E1 wave produced from all known (unclassified) types of nuclear weapons might vary by only about ten times in the energy fields they would create.[132]

---

[130]Ibid, p. 2-35
[131] Op. cit. "EMP and Space Weather and the Strategic Threat to America's Nuclear Power Stations: 2015 Final Report", p. 2-13
[132] Ibid, p. 4-6.

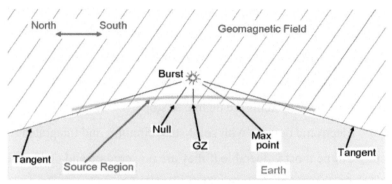

Figure 16: High-altitude nuclear detonation; E1 follows line of sight from burst point. (Source Region is point in atmosphere where E1 is formed, GZ is ground zero).[133]

Figure 17 illustrates the E1 coverage from a 500-kiloton detonation at varying altitudes. When detonated above the Earth's atmosphere, the X-rays, gamma rays, neutrons, and photon will travel great distances. These energy beams will damage and destroy orbiting satellites.[134] Note that the effects of HEMP E3 are maximized when a nuclear detonation occurs between 130 and 500 km altitude (81 to 311 miles). These altitudes are significantly higher than the nuclear detonation heights that optimize HEMP E1.[135][136] For E3, the total yield (nuclear explosive power) is most important, but for E1, the gamma ray output is the most important. As previously mentioned, the gamma ray

[133] Ibid, p. 2-16

[134] Critical National Infrastructures. (April 2008). "Report of the Commission to Assess the Threat to the United States from Electromagnetic Pulse (EMP) Attack", p. 160. http://www.empcommission.org/docs/A2473-EMP_Commission-7MB.pdf

[135] Op. cit. "The Early-Time (E1) High-Altitude Electromagnetic Pulse (HEMP) and Its Impact on the U.S. Power Grid", p. 1-2

[136] In my opinion, the data indicates that it is possible for war planners to combine both the E1 and E3 effects in a single detonation (especially if a super-EMP weapon were used) at an altitude of about 100km to 130 km, which would have the capability to bring down the national electric grind, as well as maximizing damage to the integrated circuits required to operate much of the national critical infrastructure. Several strategically placed detonations could certainly accomplish this goal.

output does increase as the total yield increases, although not proportionately.[137]

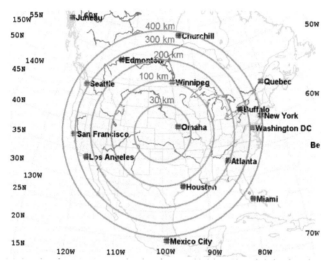

Figure 17: The red circles show the regions exposed to E1 Hemp from varying heights of burst (nuclear detonation). At 400 km height (249 miles), all of the U.S. is exposed.[138]

The optimization for E1 and E3B regarding Height of Burst (nuclear detonation) is slightly different, but it is possible to get close to an altitude for detonation what will maximize both. E3B could be a more likely choice for war planners, as they can combine the effects of E1 and E3B with a single HEMP. However, an enemy might also choose to detonate a nuclear weapon high in the atmosphere in a region far south of the U.S., which would create a massive E3A Blast Wave capable of knocking out the entire U.S. national electric grid. An orbiting satellite,

---

[137] Personal correspondence with Dr. William Radasky. Nov 22, 2022.
[138] Op. cit. "The Early-Time (E1) High-Altitude Electromagnetic Pulse (HEMP) and Its Impact on the U.S. Power Grid", p. 2-15. While higher altitudes will decrease the intensity of the E1 incident energy fields, this may be compensated with the use of a Super-EMP weapon. The higher altitude will increase the coverage of HEMP E3, which will damage or destroy Large Power Transformers and high-speed relays and circuit breakers.

which was in reality a nuclear weapon, could be used to create either scenario.

The Complexities of Electromagnetic Coupling

The process in which HEMP E1 acts to induce current into electrically conductive materials is a complex phenomenon, which is described as "electromagnetic coupling".[139] This complexity makes it virtually impossible to precisely predict the voltages that E1 will induce in a variety of circumstances.[140] [141] Consequently, many good scientists tend to shy away from making more than general predictions about the extent of damage E1 can inflict (good scientists consider exaggeration to be a sin).[142] Yet it is certainly not unrealistic to assume that many unshielded modern electronic devices (especially those connected to the grid) are likely to be disrupted, damaged, or destroyed if they are located

---

[139] "Electromagnetic signals, such as E1 HEMP, generate voltages and currents on conductors exposed to the fields. E1 HEMP coupling is like any other electromagnetic coupling. The EM fields encounter a conductor and induce voltage and current signals on that conductor. Vulnerability issues occur when the conductor connects to a circuit with parts that could be destroyed or upset." Ibid, p. 2-37.

[140] Yet the maximum peak E1 HEMP from all known nuclear weapons might vary by only about an order of magnitude, and sometimes the peak E1 HEMP from a low yield weapon can be higher than peak E1 HEMP from another weapon with a much higher yield. Op. cit. "The Early-Time (E1) High-Altitude Electromagnetic Pulse (HEMP) and Its Impact on the U.S. Power Grid", p. 4-6.

[141] The E1 HEMP field varies as a function of position, its arrival angle relative to the Earth's surface, as well as the polarization of the field relative to the cables or electrically conductive materials where coupling occurs. In other words, E1 magnetic fields are directional, and it is only the component of E parallel to the line that couples to the line. Op. cit. "The Early-Time (E1) High-Altitude Electromagnetic Pulse (HEMP) and Its Impact on the U.S. Power Grid", pp. 5-1 and 4-42. Also, personal correspondence with Dr. William Radasky, Nov 22, 2022.

[142] One example of a good scientist: Dr. William Radasky, President and Managing Engineer of Metatech Corporation, an IEEE Life Fellow and a Lord Kelvin Award Winner, elected to the National Academy of Engineering (NAE), see https://ieeexplore.ieee.org/document/9614177

within the regions exposed to E1 incident fields of 10,000 volts per meter (10 kV/m or greater), because the maximum voltages and currents induced by these fields will far exceed the rated capacity of solid-state electronics that typically at a few volts.[143]

Enormous E1 Incident Fields Created by a Single HEMP

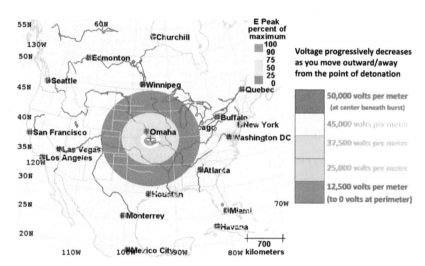

Figure 18: HEMP E1 created by 500-kiloton nuclear detonation[144] at a height of 75 km (42 miles) over Omaha, Nebraska. This plots the peak value of the incident E field total waveform.[145]

---

[143] As the devices in our modern systems become smaller, their operating voltages get lower, and their operating frequencies get higher, E1 HEMP looks to be more of a threat. The coupled signal can easily be hundreds or thousands of volts, while electronics operate at a few volts. The E1 pulse can last for many time cycles, and also have significant energy at system operating frequencies (100's of megahertz or higher). The high density of transistors and other devices on an integrated circuit means each is very small – so that even a small amount of energy can be very significant; the smaller the mass that absorbs a given amount of energy, the higher the mass's temperature increase from the absorbed energy. Op. cit. Savage et al. "The Early-Time (E1) High-Altitude Electromagnetic Pulse (HEMP) and Its Impact on the U.S. Power Grid", pp. 6-3 and 6-4.

[144] Ibid, p. 2-25.

[145] Ibid, p. 2-30. Image adapted to more fully illustrate the E Peak percent of maximum.

Figure 18 is derived from a Figure created by the Metatech Corporation[146], which illustrates the maximum possible voltages that could be induced into electrically conductive surfaces from a 500-kiloton nuclear detonation (non-super EMP weapon) at an altitude of 42 miles. Figure 18 can be used for a general approximation for the maximum E1 incident fields created by HEMP, but the maximum induced voltage and current values will not be uniform, as these maximum values will vary with position on the ground based on the weapon yield, the weapon design, and the burst height and the location of the burst relative to the local geomagnetic field.[147]

The Cybersecurity Division of the Cybersecurity and Infrastructure Security Agency (an agency of the U.S. Department of Homeland Security) issued a 2019 report entitled "Electromagnetic Pulse (EMP) Protection and Resilience Guidelines for Critical Infrastructure and Equipment".[148] This unclassified report contained Figures 19 through 21 (reproduced below), which respectively depict the peak pulse of the E1 incident energy fields created by the detonation of a 30-kiloton, 100-kiloton, and 1-megaton nuclear warhead over the United States.[149]

---

[146] Ibid.

[147] Voltage is induced to conductors via coupling of the E1 electromagnetic field to conductors, which is controlled by the amount of electric field parallel to the conductor, but also to the angle that it sweeps along the conductor and also the length of the conductor and its loads. Coupling to short cables (i.e. 1 meter) is very simple - 50 kV/m will produce a voltage of 50 kV across that meter if the field is parallel. Personal correspondence with Dr. William Radasky, March 12, 2021.

[148] Cybersecurity Division of the Cybersecurity and Infrastructure Security Agency, National Coordinating Center for Communications, February 5, 2019. "Electromagnetic Pulse (EMP) Protection and Resilience Guidelines for Critical Infrastructure and Equipment", version 2.2 UNCLASSIFIED. https://www.cisa.gov/sites/default/files/publications/19_0307_CISA_EMP-Protection-Resilience-Guidelines.pdf

[149] These Figures were created from an unclassified code called EMAT that the Metatech Corporation created for Homeland Security.

Figure 19: 30-kiloton detonation at 62 miles height induces damaging currents into 100-foot unshielded ethernet cable. The areas of yellow and red show the areas of upset and damage, respectively, to computers, phones, routers, AC/DC adaptors, and any other unshielded Ethernet-connected devices. Any other electronic devices with unprotected integrated circuits within electronic devices connected to these lines also will likely be damaged or destroyed.[150]

The red zones indicate the geographic regions where unshielded electronic devices connected to 100-foot unshielded ethernet cables will likely be damaged or destroyed by high voltages and currents induced by HEMP E1.

---

[150] Op. cit. "Electromagnetic Pulse (EMP) Protection and Resilience Guidelines for Critical Infrastructure and Equipment" from Figure 10, p. 14.

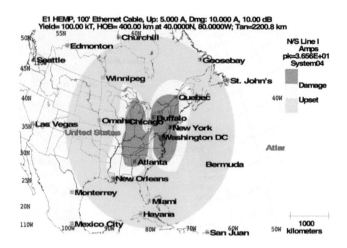

Figure 20: 100-kiloton detonation at 248-mile height induces damaging current into 100-foot unshielded ethernet cable. Unshielded modern electronic devices connected to these lines in the yellow area will likely be damaged; those in the red areas will likely be destroyed[151]

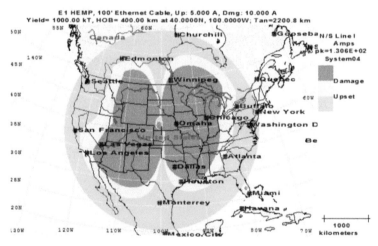

Figure 21: 1-megaton detonation at 248-mile height induces damaging current into 100-foot unshielded ethernet cable. Unshielded modern electronic devices connected to these lines in the yellow area will likely be damaged; those in the red areas will likely be destroyed [152]

---

[151] Op. cit. "Electromagnetic Pulse (EMP) Protection and Resilience Guidelines for Critical Infrastructure and Equipment", Figure 9, p. 13.
[152] Ibid, from Figure 24, p. 44.

U.S. Department of Defense Uses Software to Plan for HEMP Effects

The U.S. Department of Defense apparently accepts that HEMP E1 poses a major threat to modern electronics, as it reportedly uses classified software that predicts the HEMP E1 produced by a 100-kiloton weapon will *destroy* all unprotected integrated circuits and SCADA control units within a 9200 square mile area.[153] This area corresponds with the area described in the unclassified and authoritative studies by the Metatech Corporation, which predict peak incident energy fields of HEMP E1 will range up to 50,000 volts per meter in an area of approximately 9000 square miles. Figure 18, which is derived from a Figure in a Metatech Corporation study, also predicts E1 incident fields of 37,500 to 50,000 volts per meter in an area of 30,000 square miles, and 12,500 to 50,000 volts per meter in an area of 70,000 square miles (with the lowest voltages at the perimeter, with voltages progressively increasing towards the highest voltages in the center regions).[154]

The HEMP E1 Threat to the National Electric Grid

Although E1 poses no direct threat to the human body, E1 electromagnetic fields can induce damaging voltage and electrical currents into *any* electrically conductive object. Power transmission lines, which carry electricity long distances from electric power generating facilities, would be highly impacted.[155] The voltages and currents induced in these lines will disable or destroy the relays, sensors, and control panels found at all High Voltage Substations. This equipment controls the

---

[153] I base this statement upon my own personal correspondence with a former member of the U.S. Air University Electromagnetic Defense Task Force, Major David J. Stuckenberg.

[154] An "incident energy field" is defined as the "Field strength of a sky wave without including the effects of earth reflections at the receiving location".

[155] Op. cit. "Protecting Industry from HEMP and IEMI",

flows of electricity in and out of the Substation. A single HEMP (Figure 22) could severely damage equipment at more than 1700 Extra High Voltage (EHV) substations in the Eastern, Southeastern, and Central United States (Figure 23).[156] Simultaneously disabling these Substations would knock down the U.S. national electric grid in about half the continental U.S.

Figure 22: Exposure for E1 HEMP Burst at 170 km over Ohio[157]

[156] Op. cit. "High-Frequency Protection Concepts for the Electric Power Grid", p. 2-5.
[157] Op. cit. Savage et al. "The Early-Time (E1) High-Altitude Electromagnetic Pulse (HEMP) and Its Impact on the U.S. Power Grid", p. 7-20.

Figure 23: 1765 EHV substations at 345 kV and
higher (83%) exposed by the burst in Figure 22[158]

Destruction of Insulators on Power Distribution Lines

E1 will also impact electric power distribution lines.
Approximately 78% of all electric power is delivered to end users
(residential, agricultural, industrial) through 15kV class distribution lines,
which are likely to receive the maximum voltages and currents induced
by E1.[159] Analysis of the E1 threat by the Metatech Corporation indicated
that induced overvoltages, ranging from 200,000 volts to over 400,000
volts, would occur in these distribution lines over geographically
widespread regions.[160] There are *tens of millions of insulators on these*

---

[158] Ibid.

[159] Op. cit. "High-Frequency Protection Concepts for the Electric Power Grid", p.
2-9.

[160] Op. cit. "The Early-Time (E1) High-Altitude Electromagnetic Pulse (HEMP)
and Its Impact on the U.S. Power Grid", pp. 7-27.

lines which would be damaged or destroyed by these extreme voltages;[161] the loss of these insulators would likely cause a power grid collapse in the impacted regions.[162] (see Appendix 1)

E1 Can Induce Millions of Volts and Many Thousands of Amps in Powerlines

Under ideal circumstances (using a non-Super EMP weapon), HEMP E1 can induce peak voltages of *2 million volts* into long overhead medium-voltage power lines, which can create a current of *5000 amps* in these power lines[163] (an unclassified document from the Cybersecurity Division of the Cybersecurity and Infrastructure Security Agency states the maximum current in these lines can reach *10,000 amps*[164]). These high voltages and currents are many times larger than electrical transmission lines are designed to handle. The voltage and current signals that get generated on those lines will then multiply and move down the line, and flow into any circuits connected to the line.[165] This will allow a surge of damaging voltages and currents to enter all types of unshielded

---

[161] Personal correspondence with Dr. William Radasky, November 22, 2022.

[162] Op. cit. "The Early-Time (E1) High-Altitude Electromagnetic Pulse (HEMP) and Its Impact on the U.S. Power Grid", p. 2-11.

[163] The worst-case HEMP E1 used by the military in MIL-STD-188-125-1 for an E1-induced powerline current of 5,000 amperes. The characteristic impedance for a power line is approximately 400 ohms, thus providing a peak worst-case voltage level of 2 MV. Op. cit. "The Early-Time (E1) High-Altitude Electromagnetic Pulse (HEMP) and Its Impact on the U.S. Power Grid", p. 7-3.

[164] Cybersecurity Division of the Cybersecurity and Infrastructure Security Agency, National Coordinating Center for Communications, February 5, 2019. "Electromagnetic Pulse (EMP) Protection and Resilience Guidelines for Critical Infrastructure and Equipment", version 2.2 UNCLASSIFIED, p. 29. https://www.cisa.gov/sites/default/files/publications/19_0307_CISA_EMP-Protection-Resilience-Guidelines.pdf

[165] Op. cit. "The Early-Time (E1) High-Altitude Electromagnetic Pulse (HEMP) and Its Impact on the U.S. Power Grid", p. 4-42.

electronic devices (Figure 24). E1 can also induce large voltages and currents in low voltage cables, in lengths as short as 10 meters.[166]

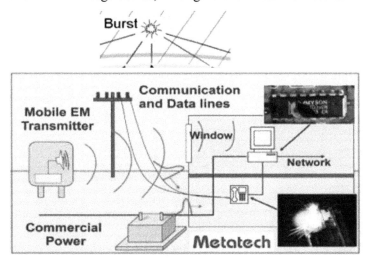

Figure 24: HEMP/EMP enters a structure via power and data lines and then enters all the electronic devices connected to this circuit.[167] This Figure illustrates EMP from a mobile Electromagnetic transmitter, as well as EMP from a High-altitude Electromagnetic Pulse.

Unprotected electronic devices that are powered on and connected to the incoming circuit are the most vulnerable, but even *an unpowered system, which is attached to cables, can be vulnerable.* An unshielded telephone line at a wall plug can receive up to 10,000 volts and 100 amps of electrical current (Table 3). With a peak E1 field of 50,000 volts per meter (found within the center of Figures 17 and 18),

[166] Op. cit. "Rebuttal to "The EMP threat: fact, fiction, and response"
[167] Figure 23 was adapted from Figure 1 from Radasky, W. (October 31, 2018). "Protecting Industry from HEMP and IEMI", In Compliance Magazine. https://incompliancemag.com/article/protecting-industry-from-hemp-and-iemi/ and
Op. cit. "The Early-Time (E1) High-Altitude Electromagnetic Pulse (HEMP) and Its Impact on the U.S. Power Grid", p. 2-16.

even a short "antenna" 10 cm in length (4 inches) can experience a voltage of about 5000 volts.[168].

Type of Conductor	~ Rise Time	Peak Voltage	Peak Current
Long unshielded wires (power lines, large antennas)	10 ns – 100 ns	100 kV – 5 MV	1 kA – 10 kA
Unshielded telephone line at wall plug	10 ns – 1 μs	100 V – 10 kV	1 A – 100 A
Unshielded AC power line at wall plug	100 ns – 10 μs	1 kV – 50 kV	10 A – 100 A
HF antennas	10 ns – 100 ns	10 kV – 1 MV	500 A – 10 kA
VHF antennas	1 ns – 10 ns	1 kV – 100 kV	100 A – 1 kA
UHF antennas	1 ns – 10 ns	100 V – 10 kV	10 A – 100 A
Shielded cable	1 μs – 100 μs	1 V – 100 V	0.1 A – 50 A

Table 3: EMP Induced Surges of Voltage and Amperage on Conductors[169]

The HEMP E1 Threat to Modern Electronic Devices

*The E1 waveform differs from E3, in that it can **directly penetrate** through apertures in the external case of equipment, such as a computer, and induce significant currents and voltages at the circuit board level.*[170] Modern microelectronics are over one million times more vulnerable to EMP than electronic systems of the 1960s and would easily be damaged or destroyed – on a regional basis -- by the EMP from a single low-yield nuclear weapon detonated high enough to cover, for example, the eastern United States.[171] Unshielded modern electronic devices with long, attached cables, are likely to be hard hit by the high voltages and currents generated by HEMP E1.[172] It seems likely that most unprotected modern

---

[168] Op. cit. "The Early-Time (E1) High-Altitude Electromagnetic Pulse (HEMP) and Its Impact on the U.S. Power Grid", p. 2-35.

[169] Op. cit. "Electromagnetic Pulse (EMP) Protection and Resilience Guidelines for Critical Infrastructure and Equipment", p. 29.

[170] Op. cit. High-Impact, Low-Frequency Event Risk to the North American Bulk Power System", p. 80.

[171] Op. cit. "Rebuttal to "The EMP threat: fact, fiction, and response"

[172] Op. cit. Savage et al. "The Early-Time (E1) High-Altitude Electromagnetic Pulse (HEMP) and Its Impact on the U.S. Power Grid", p. 6-4.

electrical equipment and electrical systems (and especially those connected to the grid) would be damaged and left inoperable in large geographic regions affected by HEMP (Appendix 1).

Integrated Circuits and Solid-State Electronics Damaged and Destroyed

The high voltages and currents induced by HEMP E1 can almost instantly damage, disable, and destroy the integrated circuits (also referred to as chips, or microchips) and solid-state electronics that are widely used in *all* modern electronic devices and control systems, which typically operate at *low voltage* (a few volts). Modern electronic devices typically contain these and are very susceptible to the high voltages and currents induced by HEMP E1 (Figures 25 and 26, also see Appendix 1).

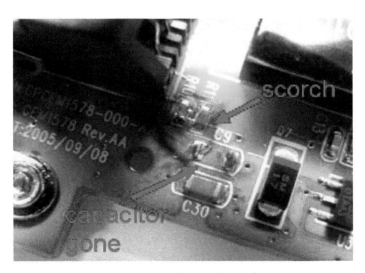

Figure 25: Capacitor damage due to large electrical pulse. The capacitor (C9) is gone, and there are scorch marks (C30 shows an undamaged capacitor)[173]

---

[173] Op. cit. Savage et al. "The Early-Time (E1) High-Altitude Electromagnetic Pulse (HEMP) and Its Impact on the U.S. Power Grid", p. 6-2

Figure 26: Integrated circuit (IC) damaged by large electrical pulse. The IC lid, normally flat, has bubbled, and is discolored from overheating.[174]

Figure 27: Modern SCADA unit. This is the SEL-2032 (front view on top, back view on the bottom).[175]

Vulnerable integrated circuits and semiconductor electronics are ubiquitous; they are used in all computers, modems, routers, switches,

---

[174] Ibid, Figure 6-3, p. 6-2.

[175] Op. cit. Savage et al. "The Early-Time (E1) High-Altitude Electromagnetic Pulse (HEMP) and Its Impact on the U.S. Power Grid", p. 7-12.

programmable logic controllers, circuit boards, solid-state safety relays, and Supervisory Control and Data Acquisition (SCADA) devices.[176] SCADAs are electronic control systems that are used for data acquisition and control over large and geographically distributed infrastructure systems. A SCADA unit (Figure 27) automatically and remotely monitors the operating state of a physical system by:

> "... *providing an ongoing reporting of parameters that either characterize the system's performance, such as voltage or currents developed in an electric power plant, flow volume in a gas pipeline, and net electrical power delivered or received by a regional electrical system, or by monitoring environmental parameters such as temperature in a nuclear power plant and sending an alarm when prescribed operating conditions are exceeded.* "[177]

SCADA systems are widely used in all parts of U.S. critical infrastructure, such as in water supply, sanitation and waste systems, all transportation systems, all telecommunication networks, all financial transactions, oil and gas refining and distribution, and power generation facilities.[178] SCADA units are also indispensable components in the controls and operations of nuclear power plants, which regulate

---

[176] Op. cit. "High-Frequency Protection Concepts for the Electric Power Grid", p. 7-7.
[177] Op. cit. "Report of the Commission to Assess the Threat to the United States from Electromagnetic Pulse (EMP) Attack", p. 3.
[178] SCADA functions include real-time measuring, reading and adjustment of voltages, currents, reactance, line status (breakers, switches, re-closers, cap breaks, voltage regulations) and transformer status as well as identifying outages and even providing means to adjust load distributions and substation maintenance.

Emergency Power Systems and the active Emergency Core Cooling Systems.[179] The 2008 Congressional EMP Commission concluded that:

> *"SCADA systems are vulnerable to EMP insult. The large numbers and widespread reliance on such systems by all of the Nation's critical infrastructures represent a systemic threat to their continued operation following an EMP event."[180]*

Super-EMP Weapons Generate Super Levels of E1

Super-EMP weapons are designed to primarily generate HEMP E1.[181] According to Russian open sources, a Super-EMP weapon can generate a peak E1 [incidence] field of 200,000 volts per meter (kV/m).[182] Russian open-source military writings claim that Super-EMP weapons generate such powerful fields that even hardened U.S. strategic forces would be vulnerable.[183] The Chinese military also describe a super-EMP weapon, stating that the E1 field "produced by nuclear EMP is about 10 to 100 kV/m and can penetrate and melt any electronic components."[184]

Note that this paper uses 50,000 volts per meter as the maximum incidence field created by HEMP E1 (see Figure 18). **In other words,**

---

[179] Op. cit. "EMP and Space Weather and the Strategic Threat to America's Nuclear Power Stations: 2015 Final Report", pp. 24 and 34.

[180] Op. cit. "Report of the Commission to Assess the Threat to the United States from Electromagnetic Pulse (EMP) Attack", Chapter 1, p. 9.

[181] Op. cit. "Rebuttal to "The EMP threat: fact, fiction, and response", p. 2.

[182] Vaschenko, A. (November 1, 2006). "Russia: Nuclear Response to America Is Possible Using Super-EMP Factor", "A Nuclear Response To America Is Possible," Zavtra,

[183] Vaschenko, A., Belous, V. (April 13, 2007); "Preparing for the Second Coming of 'Star Wars", *Nezavisimoye Voyennoye Obozreniye* translated in *Russian Considers Missile Defense Response Options* CEP20070413330003.

[184] Zhao Meng, Da Xinyu, and Zhang Yapu, (May 1, 2014). "Overview of Electromagnetic Pulse Weapons and Protection Techniques Against Them" Winged Missiles (PRC Air Force Engineering University.

this book describes the effects of nuclear weapons that produce a maximum E1 incident energy about one-quarter to one-half of the incident energy fields produced by the Super-EMP weapon described in Russian and Chinese military sources. Thus, the effects of HEMP predicted here could quite possibly be significantly more severe, especially if Super-EMP weapons are employed. Extreme cold and hot weather conditions would also increase the damage caused by HEMP.

PART 2

The Nuclear HEMP Threat to Nuclear Power Plants and Spent Fuel Pools

Summary: HEMP is a "Beyond-Design-Basis Event" for U.S. Nuclear Power Plants

The U.S. Nuclear Regulatory Commission (NRC) considers U.S nuclear power plants to be in no danger from EMP. The NRC views EMP as a "beyond-design-basis event", which does not have to be protected against with the use of "safety-grade" systems, structures, and components."[185] Consequently, no U.S. nuclear power plant (currently under license) has been designed, constructed, or retrofitted to survive an EMP attack.

The Electromagnetic Defense Task Force (EDTF), created by members of the U.S. Air Force Air University, has questioned the NRC about the lack of credible research and comprehensive physical testing of the impacts of EMP on U.S. nuclear power plants. A 2019 report published by the EDTF listed several serious concerns, including a prolonged "station blackout" (a complete loss of off-site and on-site electric power, due to the impact of HEMP on both the national electric grid and the Emergency Power Systems at U.S. nuclear plants). The EDTF took the position that *all* electronic devices at nuclear power plants are subject to EMP, yet the NRC has required *no corresponding testing* to

---

[185] Stuckenberg, D., Woolsey, J., DeMaio, D. (August 2019). "Electromagnetic Defense Task Force (EDTF) Report 2.0, LeMay Paper No. 4", Air University Press, Maxwell Air Force Base, Alabama, Appendix 1, pp. 53. https://www.airuniversity.af.edu/Portals/10/AUPress/Papers/LP_0002_DeMaio_ Electromagnetic_Defense_Task_Force.pdf

validate that the host of solid-state electronic systems and devices used throughout U.S. nuclear power plants are indeed shielded from the damaging voltages and currents induced by HEMP.[186]

All nuclear power plants rely on numerous systems that require many thousands of electronic devices (control units, rectifiers, inverters, switches, motor-driven pumps, motor-operated valves, temperature and pressure sensors, etc.) to monitor, control, and safely operate their nuclear reactors, as well as their spent fuel pools (where highly radioactive used uranium fuel is stored). These electronic devices obviously require electric power to operate; they also contain solid-state electronics that, if left unshielded are highly susceptible to damage from the high voltages and currents induced by HEMP E1. These devices are located within the various components that comprise the Emergency Power Systems and the active Emergency Core Cooling Systems (ECCS) – which will be left inoperable if there is no electric power and/or if the solid-state electronics within them are disabled.

Summary: HEMP Will Cause Meltdowns at Unshielded Nuclear Power Plants

Moments after HEMP brings down the U.S. national electric grid on a regional or national basis (see Part 1), nuclear plants located in blacked-out regions would experience an immediate loss of off-site power, which would cause these plants to shut down on an emergency basis. While emergency shutdowns do not require electrical power, the shutdowns would likely be followed by an immediate failure of the plants' emergency power systems, as well as the active Emergency Core Cooling Systems (ECCS) that require electricity and functioning motor-

---

[186] Ibid, p. 59.

driven pumps, control units, sensors, and motor-operated valves to operate. The massive voltages and currents induced by HEMP E1 would disable many of the various components that comprise these emergency systems and render them inoperable.

A large commercial nuclear reactor operating at full power will still have hundreds of millions of watts of residual decay heat in its core after emergency shutdown (decay heat is produced by radioactive fission products in the fuel rods). The core must be rapidly cooled in a matter of minutes; without functioning emergency power and active ECCS, the core will overheat and self-destruct in a matter of hours or at most a few days (this is essentially what happened to Units 1, 2 and 3 at Fukushima Daiichi[187]). Without backup electric power, restoring a forced flow of coolant through the reactor core becomes impossible. Without power, it is also impossible to maintain system control, lighting, communication, as well as ventilation to the reactor, to the emergency diesel generators[188], and to the ancillary plant[189]. And even with power, the active components of the ECCS cannot function if the integrated circuits and solid-state components within the ECCS are disabled by the huge voltages and currents created by HEMP E1.

A failure of the ECCS to remove heat from the reactor core can rapidly cause the temperature in an uncooled reactor core to rapidly reach 1204 degrees Celsius (2200 degrees Fahrenheit). At this temperature, the

---

[187] World Nuclear Association. (May 2022). "Fukushima Daiichi Accident, Event sequence following earthquake". https://world-nuclear.org/information-library/safety-and-security/safety-of-plants/fukushima-daiichi-accident.aspx
[188] EDGs have to start reliably and quickly and under any condition and must be able to take on load almost instantaneously, which generally means within about 10 Seconds. QuantiServ. (January 26, 2021). https://www.quantiserv.com/2021/01/26/nuclear-power-plant-emergency-generator-engine-block-repair/
[189] Auxiliary of power plant is ancillary equipment, such as pumps, fans, and soot blowers, used with the main boiler, turbine, engine, waterwheel, or generator of a power-generating station.

fuel rods and control materials in the core will begin to melt, leading to the complete destruction of the reactor core.[190] Because the E1 from a single HEMP could cover an area of tens of thousands of square miles, a well-placed HEMP could hit dozens of nuclear reactors at U.S. nuclear power plants with huge voltages and currents, disabling their emergency systems and causing them to all experience simultaneous core meltdowns (see Figure 38 in Part 2).

Any nation that has not protected its nuclear power plants from HEMP is at risk. For example, France apparently has not shielded its 56 operating nuclear power plants from HEMP[191]. France is not a large nation in terms of its geographic size; a single HEMP over central France could cause every unshielded nuclear reactor in France to simultaneously melt down (see Figure 39 in Part 2).

Summary: HEMP Can Trigger Destruction of Spent Fuel Pools at Nuclear Power Plants

Nuclear power plants require on-site spent fuel pools, which allow operators to safely remove used or "spent" uranium fuel rods from the reactor core during refueling operations (every 18 to 24 months) and place them into these pools. Spent fuel is highly radioactive; it must be kept constantly kept underwater during refueling and subsequent storage

---

[190] "In the absence of a two-phase mixture going through the core or of water addition to the core to compensate water boiloff . . . In less than half an hour, the peak core temperature would reach 1100 K [1520 degrees F or 827 degrees C]. At this temperature, the zircaloy cladding of the fuel rods may balloon and burst." Kuan, P., Hanson, D. J., Odar, F. (1991). "Managing water addition to a degraded core." U.S. Department of Energy Office of Scientific and Technical Information, OSTI 5642843, p. 4. https://www.osti.gov/servlets/purl/5642843 and Lochbaum, D. (March 14, 2011). "Reactor Core Cooling". https://blog.ucsusa.org/dlochbaum/reactor-core-cooling/

[191] World Nuclear Organization. (April 2023). "Nuclear Power in France". https://world-nuclear.org/information-library/country-profiles/countries-a-f/france.aspx

(5 years or longer) to shield people from its extremely lethal levels of radiation. The pools also actively cool the rods because the radiation within the rods creates a huge amount of heat, which would cause the rods to rupture or even ignite on contact with air or steam, releasing huge amounts of radiation.

Nuclear power plants require off-site electric power (supplied by the national electric power grid) to continuously cool their spent fuel pools.[192] *The pools each typically contain about 4 to 5 times more long-lived radioactive fission products than are found inside each reactor core.*[193] These pools contain some of the highest concentrations of radioactivity on the planet, yet at U.S. nuclear power plants, the pools are located *outside* of the primary containment building that houses the nuclear reactor,[194] which means they lack the "defense in depth" protection from a release of radiation that the primary containment affords the reactor core (see Figure 28).

---

[192] Off-site power is also required to run the primary cooling pumps and to restart a nuclear power plant.

[193] "Spent fuel pools at nuclear reactors contain a substantially larger inventory of irradiated fuel than the reactors. Typical 1,000-megawatt PWR and BWR reactor cores contain about 80 metric tons and 155 metric tons respectively, while their pools typically contain 400 to 500 metric tons.9 About 40 percent of the total radioactivity in spent fuel (4.5 billion curies) for both designs is from cesium-137. This is about four to five times the amount of cesium-137 in their reactor cores." From Alvarez, R. (Winter 2012). "Improving Spent-Fuel Storage at Nuclear Reactors", Issues in Science and Technology, The National Academies of Sciences Engineering Medicine, p. 80. https://issues.org/alvarez/

[194] Macfarlane, A. (2017). "Risks of Densely Packed Spent Fuel Pools", Nautilus Institute for Security and Sustainability. https://nautilus.org/uncategorized/risks-of-densely-packed-spent-fuel-pools/

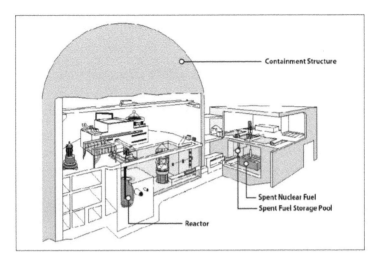

Figure 28: Spent fuel pool located outside of primary containment structure.[195] The Primary Containment Building is typically an airtight steel structure enclosing the reactor, which is normally sealed off from the outside atmosphere. The steel is either free-standing or attached to the concrete missile shield, which is designed to withstand the impact of a fully loaded passenger airliner without rupture[196]

Spent fuel pools each have large cooling systems that circulate water through the pools and remove the heat with heat exchange units. If HEMP eliminates all sources of electric power and/or disables the motor-driven cooling pumps in the cooling system, the spent fuel pools can only be cooled by pumping water into the pool.[197] If a spent fuel pool is not

[195] Werner, J. (May 24, 2012). "U.S. Spent Nuclear Fuel Storage", CRS Report for Congress, Congressional Research Service, 7-5700, R42513, p. 14. [Note, the Figure in the paper stated "Source: Timothy Guzda, Union of Concerned Scientists, modified by CRS", but no other information was provided]
[196] Nuclear Regulatory Commission. (June 12, 2009). "§ 50.150 Aircraft impact assessment".
https://www.nrc.gov/reading-rm/doc-collections/cfr/part050/part050-0150.html
[197] The Emergency Diesel Generators are to provide power to cool the reactor core, but not the spent fuel pools. Wright, D. (March 27, 2011). Where Did the Water in the Spent Fuel Pools Go?", Union of Concerned Scientists. https://allthingsnuclear.org/dwright/where-did-the-water-in-the-spent-fuel-pools-go/

continuously cooled, then, in a matter of hours or days, the water in the pool will heat to the point of boiling.[198] The water in the pool will then "boil-off", exposing the spent fuel rods to steam and water.[199]

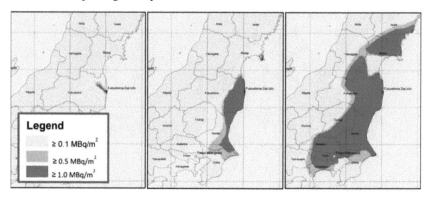

Figure 29: Left: Actual contamination levels after the Fukushima Daiichi accident. Middle: Contamination levels after a hypothetical spent fuel fire in pool starting when the wind was blowing mostly to sea. Right: Contamination levels after a hypothetical spent fuel fire in pool 4 starting when the wind was blowing toward Tokyo. This is a scenario that physically could only have occurred had there been a leak in pool. The maps show the levels of cesium-137 contamination with the red areas contaminated to above 1 MBq/m^2, which led to compulsory relocation for the actual accident. The orange areas are contaminated to between 0.5 and 1 MBq/m^2. **The huge difference in the areas contaminated above 1 MBq/m^2 in the left and right figures is due to the fact that the destruction of the roof and walls surrounding pool 4 by a hydrogen explosion *would have allowed the cesium-137 in the pool to be released directly into the atmosphere*.** In contrast, the primary containments of reactors 1–3 at Fukushima Daiichi released on average only about 2% of their core inventories of cesium-137.[200]

---

[198] M.D'Onorio, A. Maggiacomo, F. Giannetti, G. Caruso. (April 2022). "Analysis of Fukushima Daiichi unit 4 spent fuel pool using MELCOR", Journal of Physics Conference Series, DOI:10.1088/1742-6596/2177/1/012020
[199] The time to boil-off is a function of what percentage of spent fuel has been recently removed from the reactor core, as well as how much spent fuel has been loaded into the pool using high-density storage.
[200] von Hippel, F., Schoeppner, M. (August 16, 2016). "Reducing the Danger from Spent Fuel Pools", Science and Global Security, Princeton University, Figure 5, p. 148.
https://scienceandglobalsecurity.org/archive/sgs24vonhippel.pdf

If the spent fuel are exposed to steam or air, the rods will heat to the point of rupture (and ignition, in the case of rods recently removed from the reactor core) and release *massive* amounts of radioactivity.[201] If the structure housing the pool is breached (as were the buildings at Fukushima that housed the spent fuel pools, see Figure 29) and a spent fuel pool fire is exposed to the open air, the radioactive fallout released by a single spent pool fire could easily leave *tens of thousands of square miles uninhabitable for centuries.*[202] [203] Dozens of spent fuel pool fires – created by a single HEMP – could make entire states of the U.S. become uninhabitable radioactive exclusion zones.

Summary: A Solution to the Danger HEMP Poses to U.S. Nuclear Power Plants

Technology exists that could significantly reduce danger posed by HEMP to the safety systems in U.S. nuclear power plants. Adding shielding to protect the Emergency Core Cooling Systems, backup electrical power systems, and the control rooms at these plants could considerably reduce the risk of meltdown of the reactors and boil-offs of the spent fuel pools. The estimated costs to add this protection are in the billions of dollars, which is a small fraction of what the U.S. spends each year on its defense budget.

The grave dangers posed by the spent fuel pools can only be truly eliminated by (1) shutting down the reactors, which continually produce

---

[201] Alvarez, R. Beyea, J. Janberg, K. Kang, J. Lyman, E. Macfarlane, A. Thompson, G. von Hippel, F. (2003). "Reducing the Hazards from Stored Spent Power-Reactor Fuel in the United States", Science and Global Security, 11:1–51. https://scienceandglobalsecurity.org/archive/sgs11alvarez.pdf

[202] Op. cit. "Electromagnetic Defense Task Force (EDTF) Report 2.0, LeMay Paper No. 4", page 13.

[203] Op. cit. "Reducing the Hazards from Stored Spent Power-Reactor Fuel in the United States"

spent fuel (there are better ways to boil water to produce steam to generate electricity) and (2) moving the highly radioactive spent fuel to bolted-lid thick-wall metal casks designed to maintain and monitor the fuel and its containment. Thick-wall (10" to over 19" thick) metal casks should be stored in hardened facilities for security and environmental protection, as is done in other countries, such as Germany and Switzerland. Instead, the U.S. uses welded thin-wall (1/2" to 5/8" thick) stainless steel canisters inside steel lined concrete vented casks, exposed to the environment.

Unfortunately, the Nuclear Regulatory Commission has refused to recognize the dangers posed by HEMP to nuclear power plants,[204] and the nuclear utilities have to date resisted all efforts to retrofit nuclear power plants with technology that would shield against the effects of HEMP. Consequently, no steps have been taken to install equipment and modifications that would significantly reduce, if not protect, U.S. nuclear power plants from HEMP (and this is the situation in many other nations). American citizens, along with many other people in the world, remain very much at risk from the catastrophic effects of HEMP.[205]

---

[204] Nuclear Regulatory Commission. (December 2011). "Resolution of Generic Safety Issues: Issue 20: Effects of Electromagnetic Pulse on Nuclear Power Plants (Rev. 1) (NUREG-0933, Main Report with Supplements 1–35)".
[205] Op. cit. "Low-Frequency Protection Concepts for the Electric Power Grid".

Section 1

HEMP E1 Threat to Nuclear Power Plants and Nuclear Reactors

EMP [Electromagnetic Pulse] and GMD (Geomagnetic Disturbance] are part of a unique risk set which has the capability of causing systematic wide-spread failures which can lead to the simultaneous and catastrophic meltdowns at nuclear power stations and research reactors across the U.S." – "Electromagnetic Pulse and Space Weather and the Strategic Threat to America's Nuclear Power Stations", American Leadership and Policy Foundation, Final Report, 2015, p. 4.

If HEMP brings down the U.S. national electric grid, a loss of off-site power will immediately trigger emergency shutdowns of the nuclear reactors at U.S. nuclear power plants.[206] Any plant operating at full power will have a massive amount of residual decay heat (from radioactive fission products in the uranium fuel) remaining in the reactor core post-shutdown. This heat *must* be continuously removed from the core for a period of days, until the remaining heat is decreased to a low enough level that it can no longer damage the core.

Lack of cooling (forced flow of water through the reactor core) after an emergency shutdown will result in the destruction of the core and

---

[206] The Metatech corporation also states that the large Generator Step-Up (GSU) transformers that are used at nuclear power plants are highly susceptible to HEMP E3, and the catastrophic failure of GSUs could cause failure of control and safety systems at nuclear power plants. Op. cit., "The Late-Time (E3) High-Altitude Electromagnetic Pulse (HEMP) and Its Impact on the U.S. Power Grid", p. 5-1 and 5-2

release of radioactive material into the environment.[207] If the high voltages and currents created by HEMP E1 disable the Emergency Power Systems and the active Emergency Core Cooling Systems that are required by nuclear power plants to safely cooldown their reactor cores, then it is likely that nuclear plants that are unprotected from HEMP will have their reactor cores self-destruct and subsequently meltdown.

U.S. Nuclear Power Plants Are Not Designed to Withstand EMP

In 2022 there were 53 nuclear power plants with 92 nuclear reactors operating in 28 U.S. states,[208] including 62 Pressurized Water Reactors (PWR) and 30 Boiling Water Reactors (BWR).[209] All U.S. nuclear power plants and nuclear reactors are *essentially unprotected and significantly at risk from the widespread effects of an Electromagnetic Pulse (EMP).* None of these plants were designed or constructed to survive the EMP generated by a high-altitude nuclear detonation, or an Intentional Electromagnetic Interference (IEMI) device (which can be used as a powerful electromagnetic weapon at short range[210]).

---

[207] Hoffmeister, G. (2017). "Emergency power solutions for nuclear power plants – case studies, considerations, and conclusions", The Institute of Engineering and Technology, Reference Article, doi: 10.1049/etr.2016.0161 ISSN 2056-4007. http://s7d2.scene7.com/is/content/Caterpillar/CM20170217-55802-65351

[208] Nuclear Energy Institute. (Jan 1, 2023). "U.S. Nuclear Plants". https://www.nei.org/resources/us-nuclear-plants

[209] U.S. Energy Information Administration. (July 13, 2022). "Nuclear Explained: Nuclear Power Plants". https://www.eia.gov/energyexplained/nuclear/nuclear-power-plants-types-of-reactors.php

[210] The protective measures described in the paper for HEMP also apply for the EMP created by IEMI devices. Details on IEMI can be found in the publications of the Metatech Corporation and Dr. William Radasky. See Radasky, W. (October 31, 2018). "Protecting Industry from HEMP and IEMI", *In Compliance Magazine.* https://incompliancemag.com/article/protecting-industry-from-hemp-and-iemi/ and Radasky, W., Savage, E. (Jan 2010). "Intentional Electromagnetic

EMP is also not on the list of FEMA's National Planning Scenarios, so no emergency training plan for EMP exists for nuclear power plants.[211] [212] And no steps have been taken to retrofit and shield U.S. nuclear power plants from EMP because the U.S. Nuclear Regulatory Commission (NRC) regards EMP as a "beyond-design-basis event," which does not have to be protected against with the use of "safety-grade" systems, structures, components, or safety training.[213]

The NRC bases its assertion on an outdated 1982 study that says, "The likelihood that individual components examined will fail is small; therefore, it is unlikely that an EMP event would fail sufficient equipment so as to prevent a safe [cold] shutdown."[214] The NRC contends that this was confirmed in 2009 by another study done by the Sandia National Laboratory, "Assessing Vulnerabilities of Present Day Digital Systems to Electromagnetic [EM] Threats at Nuclear Power Plants ".[215]

Interference (IEMI) and Its Impact on the U.S. Power Grid ", Metatech Corp, Meta-R-323. https://www.futurescience.com/emp/ferc_Meta-R-323.pdf

[211] Report of the Commission to Assess the Threat to the United States from Electromagnetic Pulse (EMP) Attack. (April 2008). "Critical National Infrastructures", p.60. http://www.empcommission.org/docs/A2473-EMP_Commission-7MB.pdf

[212] United States Dept of Homeland Sec. (2007), National Preparedness Guidelines. http://www.fema.gov/pdf/emergency/nrf/National_Preparedness_Guidelines.pdf

[213] Op. cit. "Electromagnetic Defense Task Force (EDTF) Report 2.0, LeMay Paper No. 4", Appendix 1, pp. 53.

[214] Ericson, D. et al. (1983). "2 Interaction of Electromagnetic Pulse with Commercial Nuclear Power Plant Systems", Sandia National Laboratories. http://prod.sandia.gov/techlib/access- control.cgi/1982/822738-2.pdf

[215] Op. cit. "Electromagnetic Defense Task Force (EDTF) Report 2.0, LeMay Paper No. 4", p. 55 and p. 67.

U.S. Air Force Electromagnetic Defense Task Force Disputes the NRC

The NRC assertion that HEMP poses no danger to U.S. nuclear power plants has been contested by many experts outside the nuclear industry, as well as in the U.S. military. In 2019, a U.S. Air Academy report noted that *no comprehensive testing had been* done at operating or recently closed nuclear power plants to verify the NRC's belief that EMP posed no threat to nuclear power plants.[216] A report by the Electromagnetic Defense Task Force (EDTF), created by members of the U.S. Air Force Air University, stated:

> *"Over the last few decades, the U.S. grid and technologies that use it to function have become codependent. As a result, present design basis requirements (risk mitigation features required for individual power stations to receive operations certification) from NRC do not address EMP or GMD as a risk to nuclear power stations because stations are assumed to have constant access to a reliable power grid."[217]*

The EDTF listed a number of concerns regarding the current status of U.S. nuclear power plants, and they forced the NRC to respond to these concerns, which were:

- Lack of credible research on EMP impacts to nuclear power stations.
- Lack of comprehensive physical facility testing.

---

[216] Ibid. pp. 55-73.

[217] America Leadership and Policy Foundation. (June 2015). "Electromagnetic Pulse and Space Weather and the Strategic Threat to America's Nuclear Power Stations: Final Report", p. 14. https://www.emptaskforce.us/wp-content/pdf/Electromagentic-Pulse-and-Space-Weather-Final-Report-2015.pdf

- EMP will cause a prolonged station blackout (loss of off-site power and on-site EDG [Emergency Diesel Generator] and/or electrical distribution systems).
- EMP may impact control rooms and sensitive electronics.
- Post-shutdown EDGs may not function
- Post-EMP logistics to the nuclear power station, including diesel, would be exhausted after one week (seven days).
- Post EMP, spent fuel pools may not have adequate electrical power to the cooling pumps
- Before an EMP or station blackout, it might make sense to have more spent fuel in dry cask storage in order to reduce the risk of a self-sustaining zirconium fire in the spent fuel pool in the event of an extended loss of cooling[218]

The NRC did provide a response to these concerns but made no fundamental change in their position that the nuclear plants they regulate are in no serious danger from EMP.

Thus, no U.S. nuclear power plant (currently under license) has been designed, constructed, or retrofitted to survive EMP (or an attack with a non-nuclear Intentional Electromagnetic Interference device[219]), or an interruption of the power grid that lasts for many months (or longer).[220] No training of personal and no emergency procedures are set up to deal with the damaging effects of EMP. And many – if not most – of the circuit boards, control units, electronic devices, and system components that are likely to be damaged by the high voltages and currents induced by E1 are not stored on-site.

In 2012, following the meltdown of three nuclear reactors at Fukushima Daiichi (after they all experiences a "station blackout", i.e. the loss of all off-site and on-site electrical power), the NRC issued

[218] Op. cit. "Electromagnetic Defense Task Force (EDTF) Report 2.0, LeMay Paper No. 4", pp. 55-58.
[219] Op. cit. "High-Frequency Protection Concepts for the Electric Power Grid"
[220] Op. cit. "Electromagnetic Pulse and Space Weather and the Strategic Threat to America's Nuclear Power Stations: Final Report, p. 15.

guidance[221] which required U.S. nuclear power plants to develop strategies " . . . capable of mitigating a simultaneous loss of all AC power and loss of normal access to the normal heat sink [water used in the cooling systems] and have adequate capacity to address challenges to core cooling, containment, and SFP cooling capabilities at all units on a site subject to this Order."[222] Nuclear power plants were subsequently required to keep on-site FLEX equipment that includes portable generators, pumps, and equipment to supply reactor cooling in the event the installed plant equipment is damaged.[223] However, there is no indication that any of the FLEX equipment has been shielded against the effects of EMP.

Vulnerable Components of Emergency Electrical Power Systems

The Report of the Commission to Assess the Threat to the United States from Electromagnetic Pulse (EMP) Attack stated:

"Electronics have largely replaced all the electromechanical devices in older plants and are used exclusively in plants of the past one or two decades. Even generator exciters now have microprocessors and analog-to-digital converters. These electronics and, thus, the power plant itself are highly

---

[221] Nuclear Regulatory Commission. (April 25, 2018). "[NRC-2012-0068} Mitigation Strategies for Beyond-Design-Basis External Events". https://www.govinfo.gov/content/pkg/FR-2018-04-25/pdf/2018-08601.pdf
[222] Nuclear Regulatory Commission. (May 2012). "Diverse and Flexible Strategies (FLEX) Implementation Guide", p. 10. https://www.nrc.gov/docs/ML1214/ML12143A232.pdf
[223] U.S Department of Energy, Office of Nuclear Energy. (August 2020). "Integration of FLEX Equipment and Operator Actions in Plant Force-=On-Force Models With Dynamic Risk Assessment, Light Water Reactor Sustainability Program", p. 1. https://lwrs.inl.gov/Physical%20Security/Integration_FLEX_Equipment_Operator_Actions.pdf

vulnerable to EMP assault. Identifying and locating damaged generation plant equipment with electronic sensors and communication interdicted and/or unreliable due to EMP and repairing the system would be a complex and time-consuming process, even when personnel and parts are readily available."[224]

Should HEMP disable or destroy critical components of the emergency power and active Emergency Core Cooling Systems that are required to safely shut down the reactor, the plant operators will have to rely on ad-hoc procedures, on-the-spot innovation, and whatever equipment that would remain functional to prevent the nuclear reactors and spent fuel pools from self-destructing.

Emergency Diesel Generators (see Appendix 2)

Figure 30: Emergency Diesel Generator at U.S. Nuclear Power Plant[225] EDGs produce power in a range between 1.5 million watts and 8 million watts (1500 kWe and 8000 kWe).[226]

---

[224] Op. cit. "Critical National Infrastructures", p.35.
[225] Nuclear Regulatory Commission. (January 2011). "Chapter 09, Emergency Diesel Generator. The Generator, Exciter, and Voltage Regulation. Rev 1/11," p. 9-21. https://www.nrc.gov/docs/ML1122/ML11229A143.pdf
[226] MTU Onsite Energy, A Rolls-Royce Power Brand System. (2023). "Emergency Diesel Generators for Nuclear Power Plants", p. 4.https://aa-

Electrical power is required for a nuclear power plant to use the active components of its Emergency Core Cooling System (ECCS) and its Essential Service Water System (ESWS).[227] If the national electric grid goes down and off-site electrical power is lost, the Emergency Diesel Generators (EDGs, Figure 30) are the primary source of backup electric power for a nuclear power plant (with the sole exception of hydroelectric generating units for the Oconee nuclear plant in South Carolina). The EDG system usually has redundancies including multiple sets and twinned sets, sometimes separated by distance.[228]

The Nuclear Regulatory Commission requires that EDGs function within 10 seconds following an emergency shutdown triggered by loss of offsite power.[229] The EDGs receive their initiation signals (loss of voltage signals) from the initiation logic circuits, which, if unshielded, are vulnerable to the effects of HEMP E1.[230] The EDGs – if still functional – may not automatically start because the SCADA unit(s) that regulates them (SCADAs are found within the control room of the nuclear power plant) could be disabled, damaged, or destroyed by the effects of HEMP E1.

---

powersystems.com/wp-content/uploads/3061871_OE_Brochure_NPP_2_14_lay_ES.pdf

[227] International Atomic Energy Agency. (2019). "Passive Safety Systems in Water Cooled Reactors: An Overview and Demonstration with Basic Principle Simulators", Training Course Series 69, Vienna, p. 13. https://www-pub.iaea.org/MTCD/Publications/PDF/TCS-69web.pdf

[228] Clarke, M. (June 2020). "Battery Backup", Nuclear Engineering International Magazine. https://secure.viewer.zmags.com/publication/4d4161a2#/4d4161a2/30

[229] Nuclear Regulatory Commission. (September 29, 2011).,"Chapter 1: Diesel Generators as Emergency Power Sources". https://www.nrc.gov/docs/ML1122/ML11229A065.pdf

[230] Peach Bottom Atomic Power Station, Unit 2, Technical Specifications. (N.D.). "Emergency Core Cooling System (ECCS) Instrumentation, B.3.3.5.1.", p. 3.3-98. https://www.nrc.gov/docs/ML0211/ML021190024.pdf

The EDGs have at least four solid-state components and circuit boards that must function for them to operate: the Diesel Generator Load Sequencer, the Diesel Generator process control sensors, the Battery Charger, and the AC Static Inverter[231] (see Appendix 2). Within the EDGs are the speed monitoring and stop circuitry, the excitation systems (the system that provides field current to the rotor windings on the generator), the Fault Shutdown and Monitoring Circuits, and the Starting Circuit. There are also sensors in the cooling system of an EDG.[232] These components all utilize solid-state electronics, and if left unprotected, are vulnerable to damage or destruction by the effects of HEMP E1. The EDGs will not run if their internal circuits are disabled, damaged, or destroyed. These considerations will also hold true for on-site FLEX EDGs, although they may be somewhat less susceptible to the effects of HEMP E1 if they are not plugged into any electrical supply system.

EDGs are stored in a separate building or room, outside the control room and containment vessel,[233] whose doors may automatically lock with failure of power systems.[234] This would make them difficult to access without breaking into the room, which would add another obstacle to making the EDGs operational. Any staff attempting to get the EDGs in service would also be unable to communicate with anyone back in the control room because the communication systems would be inoperable without electricity after a massive HEMP, as would cell phones, as the electric power grid would be down, and cell towers would not function.

---

[231] America Leadership and Policy Foundation. (June 2015). "Electromagnetic Pulse and Space Weather and the Strategic Threat to America's Nuclear Power Stations: Final Report", p. 28. https://www.emptaskforce.us/wp-content/pdf/Electromagentic-Pulse-and-Space-Weather-Final-Report-2015.pdf
[232] Union of Concerned Scientists, "Nuclear Power(less) Plants", October 2015, https://allthingsnuclear.org/dlochbaum/nuclear-powerless-plants
[233] Nuclear Tourist. (Dec 8, 2005). "Key Areas and Buildings at the Nuclear Power Plant Site". http://www.nucleartourist.com/areas/areas.htm
[234] Personal correspondence with Arnie Gundersen, March 2019.

EDGs used at nuclear power plants are very large generators that require hundreds of gallons of fuel for each hour of operation.[235] [236] A typical EDG can require 400 gallons of diesel per hour to operate, which would equal 9600 gallons per day operating at full power. The NRC requires U.S. nuclear power plants to keep a 7-day supply of diesel fuel on-site to power the EDGs in case it is needed for emergency use;[237] that would equate to more than 67,000 gallons per EDG (normally two EDGS are present for each reactor at U.S. nuclear power plants). If HEMP takes out most of the U.S. national electric power grid and HEMP E1 knocks out U.S. critical national infrastructure, it could prove impossible to continue to supply nuclear power plants with huge quantities of diesel fuel if the EDGs were required to run for prolonged periods of time.

Battery Banks (see Appendix 2)

Figure 31: Battery Bank at U.S. Nuclear Power Plant[238]

[235] Earthsafe Systems, Inc. (2023). "YQA Generator Day Tanks, 07.12 How much fuel does a generator consume".
https://www.earthsafe.com/resources/yqa07-generator-day-tanks-faq
[236] A 6000 kW generator operating at full load uses approximately 427 gallons of diesel fuel per hour, see Global Power Supply. (2023). "Power Generation Calculators". https://www.globalpwr.com/power-calculator/
[237] Nuclear Regulatory Commission. (March 2007). Standard Review Plan, NUREG-0800, 9.5.4. Emergency Diesel Fuel Oil Storage and Transfer System. https://www.nrc.gov/docs/ML0706/ML070680388.pdf
[238] Lochbaum, D. (October 20, 2015). "Nuclear Power(less) Plants", Union of Concerned Scientists. https://blog.ucsusa.org/dlochbaum/nuclear-powerless-plants/

A large battery bank is a secondary source of emergency electrical power for nuclear power plants (Figure 31). If the EDGs fail to operate after the loss of off-site electrical power, the only remaining on-site source of electricity is direct current (DC) from a battery bank.[239] The batteries are normally kept charged with alternating current (AC) through inverters and chargers may use offsite power (loss of offsite power means they will be unable to be recharged, and unprotected inverters will also be damaged or destroyed by the effects of HEMP E1). The batteries are designed to supply power to emergency equipment needed to cool the reactor core for a period of 4 to 8 hours; the NRC and plant designers have always assumed that either offsite power is restored or at least one of the EDGs will be restored to operation within this time frame.[240]

Batteries produce DC power that must be converted to AC power required by the electrical system at a nuclear power plant. Nuclear Engineering International states that "Modern technology for converting between DC and AC uses large-scale solid-state electronics that is very reliable."[241] [242] The massive voltages and currents created by HEMP E1 will likely damage or destroy any unprotected solid-state electronics and integrated circuits found in the rectifiers, inverters, and the switching and monitoring systems, which are required by the battery bank to convert the

---

[239] Programmable logic controllers, which are highly susceptible to damage from HEMP E1, are also used to assign load sequences to backup electric power supplies at nuclear power plants. Gonzalez, R., Bible, C. (April 1994). "Application of PLCs for nuclear plant emergency load sequencers", Proceedings of SOUTHEAST CON '94", DOI: 10.1109/SECON.1994.324301 https://ieeexplore.ieee.org/document/324301
[240] Union of Concerned Scientists, "Nuclear Power(less) Plants", October 2015, https://allthingsnuclear.org/dlochbaum/nuclear-powerless-plants
[241] Nuclear Engineering International. (July 20, 2020). "Battery Backup for Nuclear Power Plants". https://www.neimagazine.com/features/featurebattery-backup-for-nuclear-power-plants-8037728/
[242] Nuclear Engineering International. (July 20, 2020). "Battery Backup for Nuclear Power Plants". https://www.neimagazine.com/features/featurebattery-backup-for-nuclear-power-plants-8037728/

DC current supplied by the battery bank to useable AC current. Without a functioning DC-AC interface, the Battery Bank will be unable to supply emergency power, which is required to the operate the many electrical components within the emergency systems required for a nuclear power plant to safely shutdown.

Plant Communication Systems Will Not Function Without Electricity

Emergency electric power is also required for plant communications. Without an operational plant communication system, plant operators will not be able to communicate with anyone outside the control room (as previously mentioned, landlines and cell phones will also not be operating after HEMP). The loss of instrument function will mean that plant operators will be unable to monitor water levels, temperature, and pressure within the Reactor Pressure Vessel. Operators and plant personal will also literally be working in the dark (with flashlights), as emergency power is required for lighting. If they attempt to repair any of the damaged electronics (and have the replacement parts available), they will have to make the repairs without schematics, as those are all stored *online.*

Vulnerable Components of Active Emergency Core Cooling Systems (ECCS)

Emergency Core Cooling Systems (ECCS) are designed to safely shut down a nuclear reactor during accident conditions, thus preventing damage to the uranium fuel rods and the reactor core and a corresponding release of radioactive materials. The ECCS will send water to cool the reactor in the event of a loss of coolant from the reactor cooling system. Immediately after an emergency shutdown, a forced flow of coolant (water) through the reactor core is required to rapidly remove the massive decay heat still emitted by the now highly radioactive uranium fuel rods.

There are many variations of Emergency Core Cooling Systems (ECCS) in both the Boiling Water Reactors (BWR) and Pressurized Water Reactors (PWR) that now operate in the U.S. It is beyond the scope of this paper to provide detailed descriptions of all the variations of the ECCS utilized in all these plants. However, it is possible to identify many of the components in these systems that (1) require electricity to operate, (2) depend upon solid state switches and control units to activate and control their operation (which are susceptible to high voltages and amperages generated by HEMP E1), and (3) which contain unshielded solid-state electronics and integrated circuits within their operating systems that can be disabled by the damaging voltages and currents generated by HEMP E1. The loss of electric power and/or the loss of many components that comprise the ECCS will leave all but passive (mechanical, non-electrical) components of the ECCS inoperable – leaving the reactor quite vulnerable to destruction from the decay heat that remains in the core after emergency shutdown.

Motor-Driven Pumps in the ECCS (see diagrams in Appendix 3)

The NRC describes the ECCS as "Reactor system components (pumps, valves, heat exchangers, tanks, and piping) that are specifically designed to remove residual heat from the reactor fuel rods in the event of a failure of the normal core cooling system (reactor coolant system)."[243] Emergency makeup or cooling pumps are usually motor-driven. In

_____

[243] Nuclear Regulatory Commission. (March 9, 2021). "Emergency core cooling systems". https://www.nrc.gov/reading-rm/basic-ref/glossary/emergency-core-cooling-systems-eccs.html

Pressurized Water Reactors (PWRs; 62 in operation in the U.S.[244]), the High Power Safety Injection (HPSI) System is used. The pumps used in the HPSI are primarily motor-driven and many of the valves in the system are motor-operated (Table 4).

Group	Description
AC Power	The ac buses and circuit breakers that supply power to the HPSI pumps.
Cooling	The pumps, valves, and heat exchangers that provide heat removal to the HPSI motor-driven pump and the HPSI room.
CVC Injection	The motor-operated valves and check valves in the HPSI injection path
CVC Pumps	All basic events associated with the CVC (charging; normally running) motor-driven pumps. The start, run, common-cause, and test and maintenance are included in the group of basic events.
DC Power	The batteries and battery chargers that supply power to the HPSI motor-driven pump control circuitry.
EPS	HPSI dependency on the emergency power system.
HPSI Injection	The motor-operated valves and check valves in the HPSI injection path.
HPSI Pumps	All basic events associated with the HPSI (generally lower head than CVC pumps; standby) motor-driven pumps. The start, run, common-cause, and test and maintenance are included in the group of basic events.
Special	Various events used in the models that are not directly associated with the HPSI system.
Suction	The motor-operated valves and air-operated valves in the tank suction path. Includes the failure of the tank.

Table 4: Motor-Driven Pumps and Motor-Operated
Valves used in PWR HPSI Systems.[245]

Motor-driven pumps may contain unprotected solid-state circuits that could be damaged and disabled by the effects of HEMP E1. Motor-driven pumps are designed to receive power from diesel generators (or battery banks) if power is lost from the normal power supply.[246] Such pumps will not operate in the absence of electricity, and most (if not all) receive instructions via unshielded integrated circuits within a control system that could also be disabled by a HEMP.

---

[244] Nuclear Regulatory Commission. (Sept 21, 2022). "Power Reactors". https://www.nrc.gov/reactors/power.html
[245] Zhegang, M. Kellie, K. Schoeder, J. Wierman, T. (December 2019). "Safety Study: High Pressure Safety injection 1998-2018", Idaho National Laboratory, Department of Energy National Laboratory, Table 3. p. 9. https://inldigitallibrary.inl.gov/sites/sti/sti/Sort_21672.pdf
[246] Op. cit. Nuclear Tourist. "Emergency Core Cooling Systems"

Low Pressure Pumps (2000 gpm)[247] are used in the Low Pressure Coolant Injection (LPCI) System found in BWR. The LPCI injects a coolant into the reactor vessel once it has been depressurized. Absence of electrical power and/or damage from E1 can disable Low and High Pressure Pumps along with the LPCI System.

Containment Spray Pumps used in the Containment Spray System (CSS) are mechanical pumps that don't require electricity to operate, however, the flow of spray from the pump is regulated and determined by temperature and pressure sensors,[248] which do contain integrated circuits that can be disabled as a result of HEMP E1.[249] Absence of electrical power and/or damage resulting from HEMP will likely disable the CSS.

Motor-Operated Valves in the ECCS (see Appendix 3)

Every nuclear power plant has thousands of valve actuators used in various processes and applications. The newest-generation nuclear plant has more than 13,000 valves within the plant,[250] and many types of them are motor-operated and located within the components that comprise the Emergency Core Cooling System[251] (see Appendix 3). Motor-operated valves, which regulate the flow of cooling water, require

---

[247] Ibid.

[248] Nuclear Regulatory Commission. (October 2008). "Westinghouse Technology Systems Manual; Containment Spray Systems", USNRC Technical Training Center, USNRC HRTD, p. 11.4-3. https://www.nrc.gov/docs/ML1125/ML11251A035.pdf

[249] In some cases, steam turbine-driven pumps are used (e.g. in the case of BWR High Pressure Coolant Injection system), which do not require electricity

[250] Kundin, P., "Actuation in Nuclear Power Plants", Valve Magazine, Oct 24, 2011, https://www.valvemagazine.com/articles/actuation-in-nuclear-power-plants

[251] Nuclear Regulatory Commission. (May 2010). "Theory of Operation of Motor-Operated Valves, Motor-Operated Course Manual, USNRC Technical Training Center. https://www.nrc.gov/docs/ML1134/ML11343A649.pdf

an electronic signal and electricity to open and close the valves. They will not function without electrical power or if their electronic controls have been destroyed by damaging voltages and currents induced by HEMP E1.

Pressure and Temperature Sensors

The host of electronic pressure, temperature, and water level sensors, which monitor the conditions within the reactor core and coolant systems, will not operate or send signals to the control room without electrical power. If their unshielded electronic components are damaged or destroyed by the effects of HEMP E1, they will be rendered inoperable even if power is available. Plant operators in the control room will not be able to monitor the water temperature or pressure in the Reactor Pressure Vessel. If it is possible to take manual measurements, plant personnel will have to be sent into the Primary Containment to do so and then return to the control room to report their findings if the plant communication system is not operational (no emergency power source and cell phones not working with the grid down).

Supervisory Control and Data Acquisition (SCADA) Control Units

All the various components that make up the Emergency Power System and Emergency Core Cooling Systems are regulated by at least one SCADA "Master Terminal Unit (MTU, see Figure 27)", which is found in the instrument panels and automated controls located in the reactor control room (Figure 32). The MTU uses a communication system that is connected to data interface equipment, such as Programable Logic Controllers (PLCs) or remote terminal units (RTUs);

these connect to pressure and temperature sensors, and water level sensors that monitor conditions in the reactor core.[252]

Figure 32: Kozloduy Nuclear Power Plant - Control Room of Units 3 and 4. Control features multiple consuls where data fed from SCADA systems is relayed to control room workers [253] Imagine trying to hotwire this control board in the dark, working only from memory, with no schematics.

Unshielded SCADA MTUs, PLCs, and RTUs are all quite vulnerable to the high voltages and currents induced by HEMP E1. Should the SCADA unit(s) become inoperable, key functions such as pump regulation, turbine speeds, temperature control, temperature and pressure monitoring, and electrical output would become difficult, if not impossible to measure.[254]

---

[252] Muthukrishnan, V. (April 4, 2021). "SCADA System: What is it?", Electrical 4U. https://www.electrical4u.com/scada-system/
[253] Kozloduy Nuclear Power Plant in Bulgaria., Control Room for Units 3 and 4 (1000 Mwe reactors) theywere shut down in 2007. https://commons.wikimedia.org/wiki/File:Kozloduy_Nuclear_Power_Pl ant_-_Control_Room_of_Units_3_and_4.jpg
[254] Op. cit. "EMP and Space Weather and the Strategic Threat to America's Nuclear Power Stations: 2015 Final Report", p. 24.

Passive Emergency Core Cooling Systems (ECCS)

Boiling Water Reactors

Passive systems, which are not dependent upon electrical power, are included the ECCS of all commercial nuclear reactor designs used in the United States. In 2022, there were 31 Boiling Water Reactors (BWR) operating in the U.S.;[255] BWR use the High Pressure Coolant Injection (HPCI) System, which pushes water into the Reactor Pressure Vessel (while it is pressurized) using steam turbine-driven pumps.[256] The NRC writes that the HPCI system

> ". . . *supplies adequate reactor vessel water inventory for core cooling on small break LOCA [Loss of Coolant Accident], assist in depressurization of the reactor vessel to allow the low pressure ECCS to inject on intermediate break LOCA, and backs up the Isolation Condenser or Reactor Core Isolation Cooling system under reactor isolation conditions.*"[257]

BWRs also have the Reactor Core Isolation Cooling (RCIC) System,[258] which is not considered part of the ECCS but is used during

---

[255] Nuclear Regulatory Commission. (Sept 21, 2022). "Power Reactors". https://www.nrc.gov/reactors/power.html

[256] Nuclear Tourist. (Dec 8, 2005). "Emergency Core Cooling Systems". http://www.nucleartourist.com/systems/eccs.htm

[257] Nuclear Regulatory Commission, Reactor Training Branch. (July 2007). "Introduction to Reactor Technology – BWR, Part II, Chapter 10.0, Emergency Core Cooling Systems, p. 10-8. https://adamswebsearch2.nrc.gov/webSearch2/main.jsp?AccessionNumber=ML12159A165

[258] Pressurized Water Reactors have an analogous system to the RCIC, which is a Turbine-Driven Auxiliary Feedwater Pump, which is used as a type of backup for water supply; it is not considered part of the ECCS. See Nuclear Regulatory Commission. (June 2003). "Westinghouse Technology Systems Manual, Section

normal shutdown to supply the makeup water required to maintain reactor vessel inventory (the RCIC does not have a loss of coolant accident, i.e., LOCA function)[259]. The RCIC System was among a few of the safety systems that still could operate during the Fukushima Daiichi accidents after the tsunami hit the plants. The HPCI System was found to rapidly depressurize the primary system due to its large steam release rate (ten times higher than that of the RCIC System).[260] However, neither the HPCI system nor the RCIC system were able to prevent the meltdown of Units 1, 2, and 3 at the Fukushima Daiichi nuclear power plant following the loss of all emergency backup power, and subsequent failure of all the active ECCS, following the tsunami.[261]

Pressurized Water Reactors

Pressurized Water Reactors (PWRs) have an Auxiliary Feedwater System (AFS), which has both motor-driven and turbine-driven (use steam to drive pump, no electricity required) pumps that supply additional water to the coolant system in the event of a significant Loss of Coolant Accident (LOCA). However, the AFS does not feed into the reactor core, rather it supplies water to the steam generators, so it could

---

5.7, Generic Auxiliary Feedwater Systems, USNRC Rev 0603, p. 5.7-3. https://www.nrc.gov/docs/ML1122/ML11223A229.pdf

[259] U.S. Nuclear Regulatory Commission. (October 24, 2022). "Reactor Core Isolation Cooling System". https://nrcoe.inl.gov/SysStudy/RCIC.aspx

[260] Gauntt, R., Kalinich, D., Cardoni, J., Phillips, J., Goldmann, A., Pickering, S., Francis, M., Robb, K., Ott, L., Wang, D., Smith, C., St.Germain, S., Schwieder, D., Phelan, C. (JULY 2021). "Fukushima Daiichi Accident Study (Status as of April 2012)", Sandia National Laboratories, p. 133. https://www.osti.gov/servlets/purl/1055601

[261] World Nuclear Association. (May 2022). "Fukushima Daiichi Accident". https://world-nuclear.org/information-library/safety-and-security/safety-of-plants/fukushima-daiichi-accident.aspx

not be used to create a forced flow through the reactor core after emergency shutdown.[262]

PWRs also have a passive system in their ECCS; the Cold-Leg Injection Accumulators, which consist of large volume tanks of borated water pressurized with nitrogen. (Borated water is used to absorb neutrons and thus will stop the fission process in the reactor core.) The Accumulator tanks ". . . *are designed to provide water to the primary reactor coolant system during emergencies in which the pressure of the primary drops very rapidly, such as large primary breaks.*"[263] A large LOCA is considered to be the most dangerous type of design-basis event, and the ECCS is geared towards managing this type of accident.

However, the failure of the Emergency Power System and/or the active Emergency Core Cooling Systems following a HEMP will not likely include a LOCA, so it seems unlikely that the Accumulators would necessarily be activated in this situation. This is because a failure of the ECCS to deliver coolant to the reactor core does not include a loss of coolant in the system. In fact, a Complete Loss of Flow Accident (CLOFA) triggered by HEMP would lead to rapid *increases* in temperature and pressure in the reactor core, rather than a drop in pressure in the primary coolant system, which the passive Accumulator system is designed to address.[264]

---

[262] Poloski, J., Grant, G., Gentillion, C., Gaylearn, W., Knudsen, J. (May 1998). "Auxiliary/Feedwater System Reliability, 1987-1995, Idaho National Engineering and Environmental Laboratory, NUREG/CR-5500, INEEL/EXT-97-00740, Vol. 1. https://nrcoe.inl.gov/publicdocs/SystemStudies/nureg-cr-5500-vol-1.pdf

[263] USNRC Technical Training Center, (June 2003). "Pressurized Water Reactor (PWR) Systems, Reactor Concepts Manual", p. 4-24. https://www.nrc.gov/reading-rm/basic-ref/students/for-educators/04.pdf

[264] I have written to more than a dozen nuclear engineers (including those at 8 major universities) attempting to get answers to technical questions and have received no reply from any of them.

Emergency Shutdown Following HEMP

The EMP from a single high-altitude nuclear detonation (HEMP) would bring down most or all of the U.S. national electric grid (see Part 1, E3 HEMP). The loss of off-site power automatically triggers an emergency shutdown of a nuclear reactor. An emergency shutdown does not require electricity to occur in either Boiling Water Reactors (BWR) or Pressurized Water Reactors (PWR), which are the two types of Light Water Reactors used at U.S. nuclear power plants.[265] In a few seconds after an emergency shutdown is ordered, neutron-absorbing control rods are inserted into the reactor core;[266] this abruptly stops the process of nuclear fission occurring between the uranium fuel rods (nuclear fission, the splitting of uranium atoms, is the process that creates the immense amount of heat used to generate steam to produce electricity).[267]

When a commercial nuclear reactor is operating at full power, the primary reactor pumps typically push thousands of gallons of water *per second* through the Reactor Pressure Vessel.[268] Pressurized Water Reactors can have two, three, or four primary pumps; these pumps can each pump 100,000 gallons of water per minute through the Reactor

---

[265] Bays, S., Jayoude, D., Borlodan, G. (April 2019). "Reactor Fundamentals Handbook, Idaho National Laboratory, INL/EXT-19-53301, p. 56. https://inldigitallibrary.inl.gov/sites/sti/sti/Sort_13579.pdf
Revision 0 https://inldigitallibrary.inl.gov/sites/sti/sti/Sort_13579.pdf
[266] In some Boiling Water Reactors, control "blades" are inserted from below the core; the serve the same purpose as co the control rods. Britannica. (2023). "Reactor Control Elements". https://www.britannica.com/technology/nuclear-reactor/Fuel-types#ref155173
[267] A SCRAM event does not require electricity. Neutron absorbing control rods are held in place by electromagnets above the fissile pile and upon loss of electricity the electromagnets lose their magnetism, and the rods are dropped into place bringing fission to a near halt in the core. These systems are automated and do not require human intervention.
[268] Rust, J., Weaver, L. (1976). *Nuclear Power Safety*, General Features of Emergency Core Cooling Systems, seehttps://www.sciencedirect.com/topics/engineering/core-cooling

Pressure Vessel.[269] This enormous flow of water is required to remove the tremendous amount of heat produced by the nuclear fission in the reactor core (a 3400 MW thermal output reactor boils close to 36,000 gallons of water per minute at full power).

Once the emergency shutdown takes place with the loss of off-site electrical power, the primary pumps stop. The primary reactor coolant pump or pumps cannot be restarted without the resumption of off-site power because their electrical requirements for restart are too large for on-site Emergency Power System,[270] so the Emergency Core Cooling Systems (ECCS) are required to remove residual heat in the reactor core.

Station 1 Gert Hoffmeister, Germany [5]	Station 2 Derived with an allowance for warm to hot climates
Thermal Output 4000 MWt	Thermal Output 2000 MWt
Thermal to Electric Efficiency (Net) 35%	Thermal to Electric Efficiency (Net) 30%
Electrical Output 1400 MWe	Electrical Output 600 MWe
Decay Heat 6.5% of Full Power, 260 MWt initially	Decay Heat 6·5% of Full Power, 130 MWt initially
Decay Heat 1.5% of Full Power, 60 MWt 1 hour	Decay Heat 1·5% of Full Power, 30 MWt 1 hour
Decay Heat 0.5% of Full Power, 20 MWt 23 hours	Decay Heat 0·5% of Full Power, 10 MWt 23 hours
Decay Heat 0.2% of Full Power, 8 MWt 1 week	Decay Heat 0·2% of Full Power, 4 MWt 1 week

Table 5: Examples of Decay Heat in Nuclear Power Plants after an emergency shutdown[271]

Even after the fission process is halted by the emergency shutdown, a huge amount of residual heat will remain within the reactor core. The extremely radioactive fission products within the uranium fuel rods will initially continue to produce 6% to 7% of the heat that the

---

[269] USNRC Technical Training Center, Reactor Concepts Manual. (June 2003). "Reactor Concepts Manual Pressurized Water Reactor Systems", p. 4-15. https://www.nrc.gov/docs/ML2005/ML20057E160.pdf
[270] Primary pumps in PWR range from 6,000 to 10,000 horsepower. USNRC Technical Training Center, Reactor Concepts Manual, "Reactor Concepts Manual Pressurized Water Reactor Systems", 0603, p. 4-15. https://www.nrc.gov/reading-rm/basic-ref/students/for-educators/04.pdf
[271] Clarke, M., (June 2020). "Battery Backups for Nuclear Power Plants" M.E.T.T.S. Consulting Engineers. http://www.metts.com.au/battery-backups-for-nuclear-power-plants.html

reactor normally generates while in operation (this is called "decay heat").[272] A typical commercial reactor that produces 4000 megawatts of heat (when the plant is operating at full power) will consequently have about 260 million watts of decay heat being produced by the uranium fuel in its core following an emergency shutdown (Table 5). Pressurized Water Reactors typically take 2 to 4 seconds to insert their control rods into the reactor core after an emergency shutdown.[273]

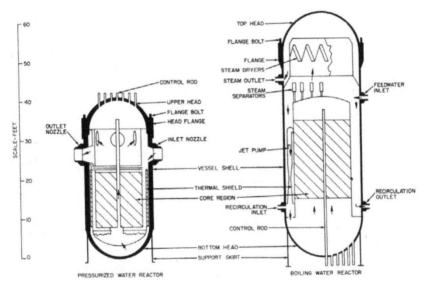

Figure 33: Comparative size of PWR and BWR Reactor Vessels.[274] In a BWR, there is normally about 16 feet of water above the reactor core,[275] which is approximately 40,000 gallons.

Hundreds of millions of watts of heat will then be trapped inside a cylindrical metal Reactor Pressure Vessel (RPV). In a Pressurized Water Reactor (PWR), the RPV may be about 43 feet tall with an internal

[272] Nuclear Power. (2023). "SCRAM-Reactor Trip". https://www.nuclear-power.net/nuclear-power/reactor-physics/reactor-dynamics/scram-reactor-trip/
[273] Ibid.
[274] Ibid.
[275] Lochbaum, D. (March 14, 2011). "Reactor Core Cooling". https://blog.ucsusa.org/dlochbaum/reactor-core-cooling/

diameter of 14 feet;[276] a Boiling Water Reactor (BWR) with approximately the same power output, will have a RPV that is around 60 feet tall (Figure 33).[277] This decay heat must be immediately and constantly removed from the core through the operation of the Emergency Core Cooling Systems (ECCS), otherwise the fuel in the core will rapidly overheat to the point of self-destruction.

In 2014, the Union of Concerned Scientists described the rate that water would boil-off in the core of a shutdown BWR when all cooling systems were not working. A week after the emergency shutdown, the decay heat from the reactor core would still boil water at the rate of 60 gallons per minute (Figure 34). If the cooling systems failed a week after shutdown (with the water level in the core at normal level) it would take only 11 hours for the water in the core to boil-off to the point where the top of the reactor core would be exposed to steam and air.[278]

Nuclear fuel uncovered by water will rapidly heat up; when it reaches 1800 °F, a chemical reaction between the metal cladding of the fuel rods and the steam flowing past will generate large quantities of hydrogen (this process is what led to the hydrogen explosions that destroyed the containment buildings at Fukushima Daiichi). The fuel rods will melt when they reach 2,200 °F.[279]

---

[276] U.S. Nuclear Regulatory Commission. (September 2009). "Westinghouse Technology Systems Manual. Section 3.1, Reactor Vessels and Internals", Table 3.1-1, p. 3.1-25. https://www.nrc.gov/docs/ML1122/ML11223A212.pdf
[277] International Atomic Energy Agency. (2009). "Integrity of Reactor Pressure Vessels in Nuclear Power Plants: Assessment of Irradiation Embrittlement Effects in Reactor Pressure Vessel Steels", IAEA Nuclear Energy Series, No. NP-T-3.1, Figure 6, p. 9. https://www-pub.iaea.org/MTCD/publications/PDF/Pub1382_web.pdf
[278] Op. cit. "Reactor Core Cooling".
[279] Ibid.

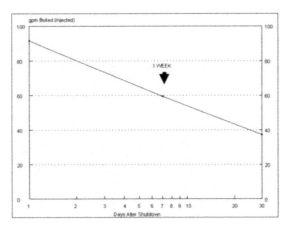

Figure 34: Rate of boil-off of coolant water in uncooled BWR core post shutdown[280]

Events Following Emergency Shutdown Caused by HEMP

As previously mentioned, loss of off-site power triggers an emergency shutdown at nuclear power plants. If off-site power is suddenly lost, all the reactor primary coolant pumps automatically stop. The massive flywheels on the primary pumps will continue to turn and push a decreasing rate of flow through the reactor core (for example, in a large PWR with four primary reactor pumps, there will be 88% of full flow 5 seconds after the loss of off-site power; this process is called "flow coastdown").[281] [282] In smaller PWRs that have fewer primary pumps, such as the AP600 with two pumps, the forced flow through the core will

[280] Ibid.

[281] Nuclear Regulatory Commission. (October 2008). "2.2 Reactor Coolant Pumps", p. 2.2-12. https://www.nrc.gov/docs/ML1125/ML11251A015.pdf

[282] There are more than 20 PWRs in the U.S. that use 4 primary reactor pumps, see U.S. Nuclear Regulatory Commission. (June 2003). "Reactor Concepts Manual: Pressurized Water Reactor Systems", USNRC Technical Training Center, p. 4-6. https://www.nrc.gov/reading-rm/basic-ref/students/for-educators/04.pdf

likely decrease at a faster rate.[283] The flow rate through the reactor will progressively decrease until in a matter of a minute or two it effectively ceases to provide any further cooling to the core.

Flow coastdown would provide some cooling to the core during short time when the Emergency Core Cooling Systems (ECCS) are normally brought online following emergency shutdown. However, if the Emergency Power System fails, the motor-driven pumps within the active ECCS, which are required to move cooling water to and from the reactor core, will not operate. If emergency power is available, the pumps, as well as the Supervisory Control and Data Acquisition (SCADA) system(s) in the control room that direct the operations of the active ECCS, may have been disabled by effects of HEMP E1. Such events will render the active ECCS inoperable.

A failure of the active ECCS to operate will lead to the loss of forced core flow (coolant water being pumped through the reactor core), thereby causing a rapid increase in reactor coolant temperature.[284] This would leave only the passive systems, which do not require electricity, to deal with the massive decay heat remaining in the reactor core. The passive systems in Boiling Water Reactors are not designed to pump coolant (water) directly into the core. As previously mentioned, the passive system in Pressurized Water Reactors (the Cold-Leg Injection Accumulators) appear unlikely to be actuated by a Loss of Flow Accident in the reactor core.

---

[283] Nuclear Regulatory Commission. (March 16, 2000). "AP600 Design Control Document, Tier 2 Manual", Chapter 15, Figure 15.3.1-1, p. 15.3-15. https://www.nrc.gov/docs/ML0036/ML003691513.pdf

[284] Foad, B., Abdel-Latif, S., Toshikazu, T. (December 2018). "Reactivity feedback effect on loss of flow accident in PWR", Nuclear Engineering and Technology, Volume 50, Issue 8, pp. 1277-1288. https://www.sciencedirect.com/science/article/pii/S1738573317304448

Complete Loss of Flow Accident (CLOFA) Caused by HEMP E1

A Loss of Flow Accident (LOFA) occurs when there is a reduction or cessation of coolant flow through the core of a nuclear reactor; it is a design-basis accident, meaning it is required by law to be considered in a reactor system's design.[285] A Complete Loss of Flow Accident (CLOFA), where there is a complete loss of forced coolant through the reactor core, is classified by the American Nuclear Society as a condition III event.[286] A CLOFA can result in damage to the fuel and ultimately the core, if forced coolant flow is not restored.

The conditions created by HEMP E1 – the loss of off-site power combined with the disabling of the emergency power systems and the active Emergency Core Cooling Systems (ECCS) – would create a condition that could be described as a CLOFA. Following the emergency shutdown and complete loss of all electrical power, neither the primary pumps, nor the secondary pumps in the ECCS could be used to remove heated water from the reactor core.

CLOFA in Boiling Water Reactors

This type of condition has previously led to the meltdown of Boiling Water Reactors at Fukushima Daiichi in 2011. An earthquake caused the loss of off-site power, causing the nuclear reactors at Units 1,

---

[285] Luangdilok, W., Xu, P. (2020). "Chapter 5 – Nuclear plant severe accidents: challenges and prevention", *Advanced Security and Safeguarding in the Nuclear Industry*, pp. 99 – 134.
https://www.sciencedirect.com/science/article/pii/B9780128182567000052
[286] Widodo, S., Ekariansyah, A., Tjahjono, H. (August 2016). "AP1000 Partial and Complete Loss of Flow Accidents Analysis Using RELAP5", National Technology Nuclear Seminar 2016, ISSN: 2355-7524.
https://digilib.batan.go.id/e-prosiding/File%20Prosiding/Iptek%20Nuklir/SENTEN_2016/DATA/681_Surip%20Widodo.pdf

2, and 3 to undergo emergency shutdowns; all three Units eventually lost all emergency power and subsequently lost the ability to move cooling water through their reactor cores. As a result, all three Units eventually had their reactor cores melt down.

The EDGs and battery bank at Unit 1 were both destroyed by the tsunami; the reactor core of Unit 1 melted down in about 7 hours after the loss of all electric power. Units 2 and 3 also lost their EDGs to the tsunami but they did have battery bank power for a limited amount of time until the batteries were exhausted. Both Units 2 and 3 subsequently had their nuclear reactors melt down within about 3 days following the tsunami.[287]

Units 1, 2, and 3 at Fukushima Daiichi were able to successfully conduct emergency shutdowns following the earthquake, which had caused the loss of off-site electrical power to the plant. These Units used their EDGs to begin the cooldown process of the reactor, which lasted about 49 to 51 minutes before two massive tsunamis arrived and destroyed all the EDGs.[288] During the cooldown period prior to the tsunami, the decay heat in their reactor cores decreased to about 2% of the pre-shutdown power level.[289] Yet this reduction of decay heat in their reactor cores did not prevent the reactors from self-destructing once all electric power was lost.

[287] World Nuclear Association. (May 2022). "Fukushima Daiichi Accident". https://world-nuclear.org/information-library/safety-and-security/safety-of-plants/fukushima-daiichi-accident.aspx
[288] Ibid.
[289] Decay heat will decrease to about 2% of the pre-shutdown power level within the first hour after shutdown and
will decrease to 1% by the end of the first day post-shutdown; it will then continue to decrease, but it will decrease at a much slower rate and will be significant weeks and even months after the reactor is shutdown. U.S. Department of Energy. (June 1992). "DOE Fundamentals Handbook: Thermodynamics, Heat Transfer, and Fluid Flow," DOE-HDBK-1012/2-92. https://engineeringlibrary.org/reference/heat-transfer-decay-heat-doe-handbook

If nuclear power plants have their Emergency Power System and/or their active Emergency Core Cooling Systems disabled by the massive voltages and currents induced by HEMP E1, they will not be able use active ECCS to reduce the decay heat in the reactor core. In other words, *plant operators will have at least 3 times more heat in the reactor cores to deal with than did the plant operators at Fukushima when they lost all electric power*. U.S. Boiling Water Reactors, therefore, are likely to be highly susceptible to destruction from HEMP E1 if they remain unshielded from EMP.

CLOFA in Pressurized Water Reactors

An article published by the International Information System of the International Atomic Energy Agency states that a Loss of Flow Accident at a Pressurized Water Reactor will cause the reactor core to be *"in a dangerous condition and the fuel elements will be damaged"* if the reactor safety systems *"do not work soon"*. The article states, *"The required protection is the reactor trip* [emergency shutdown] *followed by the adequate core cooling to remove residual heat and decay heat."*[290] If the Emergency Power System and/or the motor-driven pumps are all left inoperable by the damage done by HEMP E1, the active ECCS systems will not be able to send cooling water to the core.

As previously mentioned, the passive ECCS system found in Pressurized Water Reactors – the Cold Leg Accumulator system – may not be automatically triggered in the event of a CLOFA caused by HEMP, because the Accumulators are designed to activate following a significant drop in pressure in the primary coolant system (following a

---

[290] Suharno, I. (2007) "Core Cooling Mechanism on Loss of Flow Accident of PWR Power Reactor", International Atomic Energy Association, International Information System.
https://inis.iaea.org/search/search.aspx?orig_q=RN:45006338

LOCA). A failure of the Cold Leg Accumulators in PWRs to react to a CLOFA would mean that *none* of the ECCS in a PWR would come into play to restore forced flow of coolant through the reactor core.

Events Leading to Core Meltdown Following CLOFA Caused by HEMP

Should emergency cooling systems fail to deliver cooling water to the reactor core after an emergency shutdown, the temperatures in the core will rapidly rise to the point where the fuel rods begin to degrade. Damage to the rods can begin to occur in as little as 30 minutes, or this may take as long as one to two hours.[291] A study done at Oak Ridge National Laboratory predicted that, without any power and without coolant injection into the reactor pressure vessel "fuel is uncovered in about half-an-hour, the core meltdown begins after two hours, and the drywell electrical penetration modules fail after 4.5 hours, venting radioactive noble gas, cesium, and iodine-based fission products into the reactor building".[292]

The Emergency Core Cooling Systems are designed to provide several pathways to send cooling water to the core inside the Reactor Pressure Vessel (RPV). If these Systems fail, the water that remains in the core after emergency shutdown will continue to heat and turn to steam until the top of the reactor core is no longer covered by water. The water level in the core will continue to drop as the exposed area of reactor core quickly superheats the steam and raises the pressure in the RPV so high that it will prevent the remaining water from boiling.

---

[291] Cook, D. Greene, S. Harrington, R. Hodge, S. Yue, D. (1981). "Station Blackout at Brown's Ferry Unit One – Accident Sequence Analysis", Oak Ridge National Laboratory, Prepared for the Nuclear Regulatory Commission, Table 9.7. https://www.slideshare.net/srgreene/nuregcr2182vol1
[292] Ibid.

Figure 35: Fukushima Daiichi, Unit 3 after meltdown and hydrogen explosion[293]

The fuel rods are normally at temperatures of less than 700 °F (370 °C) when a reactor is operating at full power. As the fuel rods heat up to 1,500 °F to 1,800 °F, a chemical reaction between the Zircaloy cladding of the rods and the steam produces large amounts of hydrogen gas.[294] This process is what led to the hydrogen explosions that destroyed the secondary containment buildings at Fukushima Daiichi (Figure 35).

Once the temperature of the fuel rods reaches 1,290 °F to 1650 °F (700 °C to 900 °C), the Zircaloy cladding of the rods will deform; if the pressure inside the RPV has been lowered through venting (via an emergency relief valve or pressure disc),[295] the internal pressure of the

[293] IAEA Imagebank, CC BY-SA 2.0 <https://creativecommons.org/licenses/by-sa/2.0>, via Wikimedia Commons. https://commons.wikimedia.org/wiki/File:Mike_Weightman_(02810459).jpg
[294] Lochbaum, D. (April 5, 2016). "Reactor Core Damage: Meltdown", Union of Concerned Scientists. https://blog.ucsusa.org/dlochbaum/reactor-core-damage-meltdown/
[295] Steinkamp, H. (1995). "Emergency Venting of Pressure Vessels", International Atomic Energy Association, International Information System.

fuel rods will cause the Zircaloy cladding to rupture, and this will release highly radioactive gases from inside the rods. If the RPV has maintained high-pressure, the Zircaloy will remain on the rods and form a uranium dioxide-zirconium eutectic with a melting point of 1,200 °C to 1,400 °C (2,190 °F to 2,550° F).

An exothermic reaction between steam and zirconium can also take place, which can become self-sustaining (a Zircaloy fire) that produces hydrogen. When temperatures in the core reach 1,300 °C to 1,500 °C (2,370 °F and 2,730 °F), the Zircaloy rod cladding evaporates.[296] When the fuel rods reach the temperatures where they rupture or ignite, highly radioactive gases and fission products (iodine, krypton, and cesium) are released into the RPV. Virtually all the radioactive cesium in the rods will be converted to a gas,[297] which is why it becomes the predominant radioisotope in the fallout from catastrophic accidents at nuclear power plants where fuel rods are ruptured and/or ignited.[298]

---

https://inis.iaea.org/collection/NCLCollectionStore/_Public/28/005/28005402.pdf
[296] Libmann, J. (1996). "Elements of nuclear safety". L'Editeur : EDP Sciences. p. 194. ISBN 2-86883-286-5 and Kolev, N. (2009). "Multiphase Flow Dynamics 4: Nuclear Thermal Hydraulics", Volume 4. Springer. p. 501. ISBN 978-3-540-92917-8.
[297] Cesium is the second most volatile element after mercury; it becomes a gas at 1240°F (671°C).
[298] Cesium-137, which has a 30-year half-life, appears in the key of maps that define the radiation control and exclusion zones of Chernobyl and Fukushima, see https://www.nature.com/articles/srep01742/figures/3
https://en.wikipedia.org/wiki/File:Chernobyl_radiation_map_1996.svg

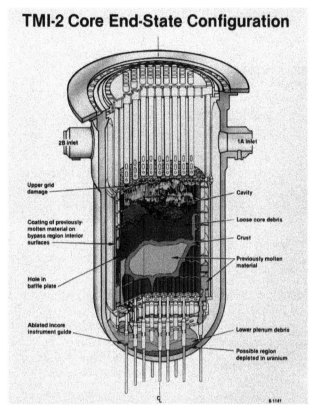

TMI-2 Core End-State Configuration

2B inlet — 1A inlet

Upper grid damage — Cavity

Coating of previously-molten material on bypass region interior surfaces — Loose core debris

— Crust

— Previously molten material

Hole in baffle plate

Ablated incore instrument guide — Lower plenum debris

— Possible region depleted in uranium

Figure 36: The meltdown of the Three Mile Island nuclear reactor destroyed the Reactor Pressure Vessel (RPV); the corium almost breached the Vessel and fell onto the containment floor below the reactor[299]

When temperatures in the core reach 2,700 °C to 2,800 °C (4,890 °F to 5,070 °F) the uranium oxide fuel rods melt and the reactor core structure collapses.[300] The lava-like molten uranium fuel, called "corium", will move to the bottom of the Reactor Pressure Vessel (Figure 36). When the core of the reactors at Units 1, 2, and 3 in Fukushima Daiichi melted down, the corium broke through the bottom of the RPVs and then it destroyed the concrete beneath the RPV, allowing the

---

[299] Op. cit. "Reactor Core Damage: Meltdown", Figure 4.
[300] Op. cit. "Elements of nuclear safety".

radiation to reach the groundwater and then the Pacific Ocean (Figure 37).

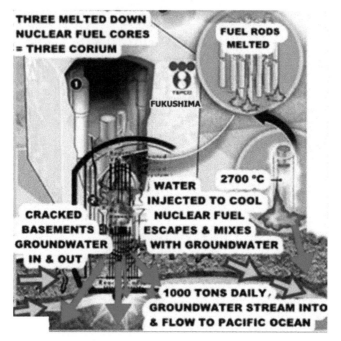

Figure 37: Illustration of Fukushima Daiichi melted cores forming corium, breaching the RPV, cracking concrete below, with radiation entering groundwater and Pacific Ocean.[301]

Because the high voltages and currents induced by E1 from a single HEMP could damage and destroy solid-state electronics in an area of tens of thousands of square miles, *a well-placed HEMP could hit dozens of nuclear reactors at U.S. nuclear power plants located within an E1-affected region.* Dozens of reactors at U.S. nuclear power plants could simultaneously experience core meltdowns (Figure 38).

---

[301] Teres, F. (March 4, 2016)

**3 Nuclear Bursts Create 3 Circular Zones (in red)
Where E1 levels Can Lead to Meltdown of Nuclear Reactors**

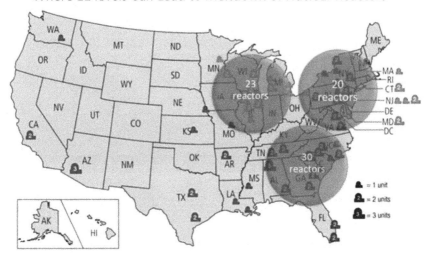

Figure 38: The number of operating nuclear reactors (20 to 30 in each zone) that would be within the areas predicted to have HEMP E1 levels of 12,500 volts per meter or greater; each zone is created by one 500-kiloton warhead detonated at an altitude of 75 km (42 miles).[302]

Other nations beside the U.S. also appear to have failed to shield their nuclear reactors from HEMP. France could have *all* its nuclear reactors at risk from a single HEMP (from a non-Super EMP nuclear weapon). One HEMP would blanket all of France with E1 incident energy fields capable of inducing high voltages and currents that would disable the Emergency Power System and active Emergency Core Cooling Systems at *every* unshielded French nuclear power plant (Figure 39). The subsequent meltdown of the reactors and likely destruction of

---

[302] Map of nuclear power plants from the NRC
https://www.nrc.gov/reactors/operating/map-power-reactors.html based upon the data on Peak E1 provided by the Metatech Corporation. Op. cit. "The Early-Time (E1) High-Altitude Electromagnetic Pulse (HEMP) and Its Impact on the U.S. Power Grid", p. 2-30.

their spent fuel pools would leave France – and probably much of Europe – an uninhabitable radioactive wasteland.

One HEMP Can Destroy Every Nuclear Reactor In France

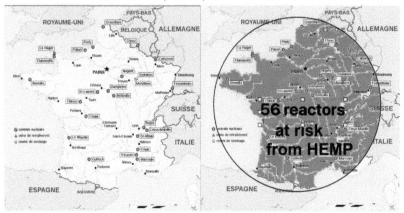

Figure 39: Fifty-six French unshielded nuclear reactors would be within the areas predicted to have HEMP E1 levels of 12,500 volts per meter or greater created by a single HEMP produced by one 500-kiloton warhead detonated at an altitude of 75 km (42 miles).[303]

---

[303] Map of French nuclear power plants from Wikimedia, by Eric Gaba – Wikimedia Commons user: Sting

Section 2

Vulnerabilities of Spent Fuel Pools to nuclear HEMP

> *"If response organizations cannot provide timely support in terms of restoration of electrical power due to logistical interruption or issues with control systems (caused by EMS [EMP and GMD] impacts), in some cases, stations would have roughly 16 hours of battery power to continue cooling reactors and spent fuel pools. **In a worst-case scenario, all reactors within an affected region could be impacted simultaneously. In the United States, this would risk meltdowns at approximately 60 sites and 99 nuclear reactors, with more than 60,000 metric tons of spent nuclear fuel in storage pools.** Prolonged loss of power to these critical sites poses a risk of radioactive contamination to the Continental United States with consequentially disastrous impact to the economy and public health."*
>
> – "Electromagnetic Task Force 2018 Report", U.S. Air Force, Air University Press, Lemay Paper Number 2, page 9.[304]

---

[304] Op. cit. Electromagnetic Defense Task Force (EDTF)", Air University Press Maxwell Air Force Base, Alabama, LeMay Paper No. 2.

High-level Radioactive Waste in Spent Fuel Pools

Commercial nuclear reactors undergo refueling about every 12 to 18 months, when unused uranium fuel rods are loaded into the reactor core after the highly radioactive "spent fuel" (uranium fuel rods that have undergone nuclear fission) is removed from the core (about one-third of the rods in the reactor core are typically replaced during each refueling). Unused uranium fuel rods can be handled without danger but spent fuel rods are intensely radioactive and highly lethal. Spent fuel gives off about 1 million rems (10,00Sv) of radiation per hour, which is enough radiation to kill a person who is next to the rods in a matter of seconds. For about the first 100 years after coming out of the reactor, spent fuel emits gamma radiation at a dose rate greater than 1 sievert per hour, which would be lethal to about 50% of adults in three to four hours.[305]

During refueling operations, the intensely radioactive spent fuel is robotically removed from the top of the Reactor Pressure Vessel through a refueling cavity that is filled with water; the fuel is then transferred through water-filled transfer canals or tubes to at-reactor[306] spent fuel pools.[307] In U.S. Boiling Water Reactors, these pools are located outside primary containment within the reactor building (secondary containment). U.S. Pressurized Water Reactors also have their spent fuel pools located outside primary containment, adjacent to it in a

---

[305] Alvarez, R. (May 2011). "Spent Nuclear Fuel Pools in the U.S.: Reducing the Deadly Risks of Storage", Institute for Policy Studies, Washington D.C. Retrieved from https://www.nrc.gov/docs/ML1209/ML120970249.pdf
[306] There are also "away-from-reactor" spent fuel pools, which contain spent fuel that has significantly less radioactive and less thermally hot used fuel rods.
[307] Nuclear Energy Agency, Committee on the Safety of Nuclear Installations. (May 4, 2015). "Status Report on Spent Fuel Pools Under Loss-of-Cooling and Loss-of-Coolant Accident Conditions, Final Report", p. 32. https://www.oecd-nea.org/jcms/pl_19596/status-report-on-spent-fuel-pools-under-loss-of-cooling-and-loss-of-coolant-accident-conditions-final-report

separate fuel handling building or auxiliary building (also secondary containment).[308]

The pools are typically about 12 meters (36 feet) deep; they vary in width and length, depending on the reactor size, and are constructed of reinforced concrete with a stainless-steel liner to prevent leakage and maintain water quality. The fuel is stored in stainless steel racks that are submerged in about 7 meters (21 feet) of water.[309] Both the water in the pool and the thick concrete walls act to shield people from the intense radiation of the rods.

Spent fuel generates the most heat and radioactivity when it is first removed from the reactor core. The Nuclear Energy Agency states that "the maximum thermal power released from all spent fuel in the pool is typically about 0.3 % of the reactor thermal power (e.g., 10 MW for a 900 MWe reactor).[310] This heat will decrease with time, but it must be constantly cooled by a dedicated cooling system. The spent fuel cooling systems can accept backup emergency power from EDGs.[311] However, it is not clear whether or not the EDGs at nuclear plants, which are designated to support the plant safety systems (ECCS, communication, and lighting systems, etc.), are also designated to support the spent fuel pools. FLEX emergency diesel generators may have been given that assignment. It is also unclear if all U.S. nuclear power plants store FLEX generators (and pumps) on-site, as there are regional storage centers set up to supply nuclear power plants within their defined service regions.

---

[308] Ibid, p. 25.
[309] Ibid.
[310] Ibid, p. 21.
[311] Ibid, p. 34.

On-Site Storage of Spent Fuel at Nuclear Power Plants

U.S. nuclear power plants store most of their spent fuel on-site. As of 2021, U.S. Department of Energy data showed that the U.S. had created close to 85,000 tons of spent nuclear fuel.[312] Spent fuel must remain in the pool for 5 to 6 years (or longer for the "high-burnup" fuel rods now in use) until its radioactivity and corresponding thermal heat declines enough to permit relatively safe removal from the pool and subsequent transport to interim storage (which typically is also on-site; the fuel assemblies are placed inside steel containers, which are welded shut and then encased in concrete, and placed above or below ground). About half of the total inventory of spent fuel remains in the pools, while the other half has been removed from the pools and placed in dry cask storage.[313]

Spent fuel pools were originally designed to hold slightly more than the contents of one reactor core's inventory, because there initially were no plans for long-term on-site storage.[314] A federal geologic long-term repository for the fuel was planned and built in Nevada, but because the site was poorly chosen, due to political considerations (in court it was found that the site had serious problems with "hydrology, inadequacy of the proposed waste package, repository design, and volcanism"),[315] the Yucca Mountain Nuclear Waste Repository was never opened. There

---

[312] Walton, R. (April 1, 2021). "Just the Stats: Volume of U.S. spent nuclear fuel totals 85K metric tons since 1968", Power Engineering. https://www.power-eng.com/nuclear/just-the-stats-volume-of-u-s-spent-nuclear-totals-85k-metric-tons-since-1968/#gref

[313] Alvarez, R. (November 13, 2020). "What Congress Needs to Know About Pending Nuclear Waste Legislation", Environmental and Energy Study Institute. https://www.eesi.org/briefings/view/111320nuclear

[314] Kadak, A. (June 15, 2012). "Storage of Spent Nuclear Fuel, National Academy of Engineering. https://www.nae.edu/59226/Storage-of-Spent-Nuclear-Fuel

[315] State of Nevada. (2023). "The Fight Against Yucca Mountain". https://ag.nv.gov/Hot_Topics/Issue/Yucca/

were also plans to reprocess the spent fuel to extract plutonium, but concerns about nuclear weapons proliferation, as well as many serious health and environmental problems associated with plutonium reprocessing, ended these plans in 1977.[316]

Figure 40: Spent Fuel Pool at Unit 2 of New Brunswick Nuclear Power Plant in Southport, N.C.[317]

Consequently, on-site spent fuel storage was expanded at the nuclear power plants by utilizing high-density storage in the fuel pools. All U.S. spent fuel pools now hold at least 3 to 5 times more radioactivity than is found in a reactor core (by 2013, some pools contained the

---

[316] Walsh, E. (April 8, 1977). "Carter Acts to Curb the Spread of Plutonium", The Washington Post.
https://www.washingtonpost.com/archive/politics/1977/04/08/carter-acts-to-curb-spread-of-plutonium/ef0ef035-b6e6-4b90-94e3-c3109d2692eb/
[317] By Nuclear Regulatory Commission from US - Spent Fuel Pool of Unit 2 at Brunswick Nuclear Power Plant, Public Domain,
https://commons.wikimedia.org/w/index.php?curid=65649227

equivalent of nearly 9 reactor cores of spent fuel).[318] The greatly increased density of the fuel in the pools makes it impossible to cool the fuel by natural circulation of the water, which means pool cooling systems have to be kept running constantly to prevent overheating of the pools (Figure 40).

These pools represent some of the highest concentrations of radioactivity on the planet.[319] Roughly 40% of the total radioactivity in spent fuel is emitted by Cesium-137 – a highly radioactive fission product with a 30-year half-life.[320] Cesium-137 appears to be the primary long-term environmental contaminant from the meltdown of the nuclear reactors at the Chernobyl and Fukushima nuclear power plants;[321] tens of thousands of square miles hit by fallout became radiation control zones, and about 2827 square kilometers (1100 square miles) remain an uninhabitable radiation exclusion zone from the Chernobyl disaster.

The key within the 1996 map of the destroyed Chernobyl nuclear plant (Figure 41) shows that the contamination of a square kilometer of land with 40 Curies of Cesium-137 is what qualifies that land to be classified as an uninhabitable closed/exclusion zone. There are 88 Curies *per gram* of Cesium-137, so *less than half a gram* of Cesium-137, made into an aerosol and distributed over a square kilometer (1.2 grams per

---

[318] Statement of David Lochbaum, Director, Nuclear Safety Project, Before the Senate Committee
on Energy and Natural Resources. (July 20, 2013).
https://www.energy.senate.gov/services/files/89dbc888-171c-4f77-8ecf-83a0055fcfb9
[319] Op. cit. "Spent Nuclear Fuel Pools in the U.S.: Reducing the Deadly Risks of Storage"
[320] Op. cit. "What Congress Needs to Know About Pending Nuclear Waste Legislation"
[321] The water-soluble form of cesium becomes ubiquitous in contaminated ecosystems and is recycled by plants and animals because it is in the same atomic family as potassium, which is a macronutrient.

square mile), will leave that land uninhabitable for at least a century.[322]
1.2 grams is less than half the weight of a U.S. dime.

Figure 41: Map of Chernobyl Radiation Control and Closed
Zones in 1996[323] Less than half of one gram of Cesium-137
can make a square kilometer uninhabitable.

---

[322] Cesium-137 has a 30-year half-life; after 10 half-lives, about 1/1000 of the
original total would remain.
[323] CIA Factbook, Sting (vectorisation), MTruch (English translation),
Makeemlighter (English translation) -
http://www.lib.utexas.edu/maps/belarus.html, specifically
http://www.lib.utexas.edu/maps/commonwealth/chornobyl_radiation96.jpg and

Comparison of Cesium-137 Inventories
(Curies)

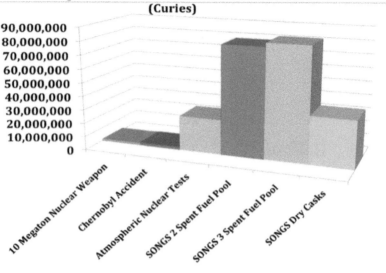

Figure 42: Cesium-137 in individual spent fuel pools
2 and 3 at San Onofre Nuclear Generating Station
(SONGS). SONGS 2 and SONGS 3 Spent Fuel Pools
contained 89 times more Cesium-137 than was
released by the exploded Chernobyl reactor.[324]

The fuel rods in *each* U.S. spent fuel pool contain many hundreds
of kilograms/pounds of cesium-137. The Chernobyl incident did not
involve a spent fuel pool; it was the reactor that exploded, which released
cesium-137 inventories with 1.89 million Curies of radiation. This left an
area half the size of New Jersey uninhabitable. In comparison, Unit 3 of
the closed San Onofre Nuclear Power Plant in San Diego contains
cesium-137 inventories amounting to 61.6 million curies of radiation –

File: Tchernobyl_radiation_1996.svg for the vector version, CC BY-SA 2.5,
https://commons.wikimedia.org/w/index.php?curid=2628661
[324] Alvarez, R. (June 25, 2013). "Reducing the hazards of high-level radioactive
waste in Southern California: Storage of spent nuclear fuel at San Onofre",
Friends of the Earth, p. 4.
https://sanonofresafety.files.wordpress.com/2018/06/songs_spent_fuel_final-
alvarez.pdf

more than 30 times the amount of cesium-137 released by Chernobyl (Figure 42).[325]

Vulnerabilities of Spent Fuel Pools to Long-term Loss of Power

Should HEMP bring down the national electric grid, nuclear power plants would be left without off-site electrical power, which they require to continuously operate the cooling systems used to cool their spent fuel pools. If the Emergency Power System at the nuclear plant is damaged by HEMP and fails to operate, the large amounts of heat given off by the spent fuel will, in a matter of days or weeks, cause the water in the pools to heat to the point of boiling – unless the cooling systems at the pools can accept electric power from backup generators, or unless water can be pumped back into the pools on a routine basis. This would require working (undamaged) diesel generators, pumps and a supply of diesel fuel that perhaps would need to be sufficient to run the generators or pump water into the spent fuel pools for months.[326]

Nuclear power plants are currently required to store only a week's worth of diesel fuel on site, and this is for the purpose of running the emergency diesel generators to power the plant lighting, communication systems, and Emergency Core Cooling Systems needed to safely cooldown the reactor core.[327] In 2018, a report from the U.S. Air Force Air Academy warned that *"Extended electrical power loss to nuclear power plants can lead to widespread radioactive contamination from the overheating of on-site spent fuel pools and breach of reactor*

---

[325] Op. cit. "Spent Nuclear Fuel Pools in the U.S.: Reducing the Deadly Risks of Storage"

[326] If FLEX equipment is kept on-site, it may include pumps that can be used to pump water into the spent fuel pools.

[327] Nuclear Regulatory Commission, REGULATORY GUIDE 1.137 (July 2012). "Fuel Oil Systems for Emergency Power Supplies". https://www.nrc.gov/docs/ML1230/ML12300A122.pdf

containment at more than 60 sites and affect U.S. military installations."[328] To reduce this danger, the report recommended that EMP-hardened generators and at least 30 days' worth of additional fuel (on-site) be supplied for the generators, in conjunction with the transferring of spent fuel to dry cask storage.[329]

Consequences of Loss of Cooling in Spent Fuel Pools

If HEMP should knock out the U.S. national electric grid and act to seriously damage and disable the Emergency Power System at a nuclear power plant, in a matter of hours or days, the water in the spent fuel pool will heat to the point of boiling.[330] The water in the pool will then "boil-off", exposing the spent fuel rods to steam and water.[331] Exposure to steam or air would cause the zirconium alloy cladding on rods to heat to the point of rupture, which would allow the release of highly radioactive gases.

U.S. spent fuel pool are densely packed with spent fuel rods, making them quite susceptible to spent fuel pool fires. If the pool contains fuel rods that have been removed from the core during the previous six to twelve months, the exposed rods may heat to the point of

---

[328] Stuckenberg, D., Woolsey, J., DeMaio, D. (November 2018). "Electromagnetic Defense Task Force (EDTF)", Air University Press Maxwell Air Force Base, Alabama, LeMay Paper No. 2, p. 32. https://www.airuniversity.af.edu/Portals/10/AUPress/Papers/LP_0002_DeMaio_ Electromagnetic_Defense_Task_Force.pdf

[329] Ibid

[330] M.D'Onorio, A. Maggiacomo, F. Giannetti, G. Caruso. (April 2022). "{Analysis of Fukushima Daiichi unit 4 spent fuel pool using MELCOR", Journal of Physics Conference Series, DOI:10.1088/1742-6596/2177/1/012020

[331] The time to boil-off is a function of what percentage of spent fuel has been recently removed from the reactor core, as well as how much spent fuel has been loaded into the pool using high-density storage.

ignition,[332] leading to a propagating fuel rod fire that would involve all the rods the pool.[333]

In 2003, a peer-reviewed article, published by the international journal *Science and Global Security*, described the dangers of "dense-packed" spent fuel:

> *"It has been known for more than two decades that, in case of a loss of water in the pool, convective air cooling would be relatively ineffective in such a "dense-packed" pool. Spent fuel recently discharged from a reactor could heat up relatively rapidly to temperatures at which the zircaloy fuel cladding could catch fire and the fuel's volatile fission products, including 30-year half-life 137Cs [Cesium-137], would be released. The fire could well spread to older spent fuel. The long-term land-contamination consequences of such an event could be significantly worse than those from Chernobyl."[334]*

U.S. spent fuel pools are located *outside* of the massive concrete primary containment building that houses the nuclear reactor (unlike Russian

---

[332]Rods more recently removed from the reactor – within 6 to 12 months – produce enough heat from radioactive decay to ignite a strongly exothermic reaction if exposed to steam or air, which burns at temperatures of thousands of degrees F and spread throughout the pool, see Safety and Security of Commercial Spent Nuclear Fuel Storage: Public Report (2006), National Academies of Sciences, pp. 38-39, see http://nap.edu/11263

[333] Op. cit. "Reducing the Hazards from Stored Spent Power-Reactor Fuel in the United States"

[334] Alvarez, R. Beyea, J. Janberg, K. Kang, J. Lyman, E. Macfarlane, A. Thompson, G. von Hippel, F. (2003). "Reducing the Hazards from Stored Spent Power-Reactor Fuel in the United States", Science and Global Security, 11:1–51, pp. 1-2. https://www.nrc.gov/docs/ML1209/ML120960695.pdf

nuclear power plants), so the pools do *not* have a steel-lined, concrete barrier like the ones that cover the reactor buildings to prevent the escape of radioactivity. A significant number of the secondary containment buildings for spent fuel are not robust structures. A former Senior Policy Advisor to the Secretary of Energy in the Clinton Administration states, *"U.S. spent nuclear fuel pools are mostly contained in ordinary industrial structures designed to merely protect them against the elements. Some are made from materials commonly used to house big-box stores and car dealerships."*[335]

A single spent pool fire could release huge amounts of radiation that could leave tens of thousands of square miles uninhabitable for a century or longer.[336] [337] Figure 43 illustrates the possible consequences of a *single* spent fuel pool fire. *Dozens of spent fuel pool fires – created by a single HEMP – could turn vast areas of the U.S. into uninhabitable radioactive exclusion zones.*

---

[335] Op. cit. "Spent Nuclear Fuel Pools in the U.S.: Reducing the Deadly Risks of Storage", p. 1.
[336] Op. cit. "Electromagnetic Defense Task Force (EDTF) Report 2.0, LeMay Paper No. 4", p. 13.
[337] Op. cit. "Reducing the Hazards from Stored Spent Power-Reactor Fuel in the United States"

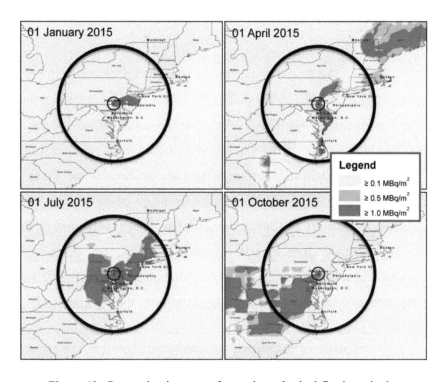

Figure 43: Contamination areas from a hypothetical fire in a single high-density spent fuel pool at the Peach Bottom Nuclear Power Plant in Pennsylvania releasing 1600 PBq of Cesium-137 on four dates in 2015. NRC cost-benefit analyses do not include the benefits of reduced population relocations and radiation doses beyond 50 miles (80 km) shown by the small circles. The large (540-km or 335-mile) radius circles show the average maximum distance out to which the NRC staff found that long-term relocations would be necessary for a 1090 PBq (29 MCi) release of Cesium-137. The NRC has not released such detailed information for a 1600 PBq release. The wind in this region tends to blow toward the Atlantic Ocean but the site is inland and there are major urban areas along the coast. Densely populated areas therefore would be downwind from Peach Bottom relatively frequently. Square corners in some deposition patterns are artifacts due to the fact that the meteorological data is provided on a 0.5- degree grid.[338]

---

[338] Op. cit. "Reducing the Danger from Spent Fuel Pools", Figure 6, p. 155.

Reduce the Danger of Catastrophic Release of Radiation from Spent Fuel Pools

The grave dangers posed by the spent fuel pools can only be completely eliminated by (1) shutting down the reactors, which produce a continual stream of this high-level nuclear waste and (2) moving the existing highly radioactive spent fuel to bolted lid thick-wall metal casks designed to maintain and monitor the fuel and its containment. Thick-wall (10" to over 19" thick) metal casks should be stored in hardened facilities for security and environmental protection, as is done in other countries, such as Germany and Switzerland. Instead, the U.S. uses welded thin-wall (1/2" to 5/8" thick) stainless steel canisters inside steel lined concrete vented casks, which are exposed to the environment.

Comparison of Spent Fuel Storage Impacts (unspecified cooling loss)		
Impacts	Spent Fuel Pool Storage	Dry Cask Storage
Population Displaced	4,100,000	800,000
Landmass Contamination	94,000 sq. miles	170 sq. miles
Radioactive Contaminates Released	8.8 MCI of Ce-137	.8 MCI of Ce-137

Sources: National Academy of Sciences, "Lessons Learned from the Fukushima Nuclear Accident for Improving Safety and Security of U.S. Nuclear Plants Phase 2," 2016, based on data from the Nuclear Regulatory Commission, NUREG-2161, "Consequence Study of Beyond-Design Basis Earthquake Affecting the Spent Fuel Pool for a U.S. Mark I Boiling Water Reactor," September 2014

Figure 44: Removing spent nuclear fuel from fuel pools and putting it into dry cask storage could greatly reduce displaced populations in a worst-case scenario with U.S spent fuel pools losing the ability to keep spent fuel cool[339]

The U.S. Air Force Air Academy published a study that showed the importance of using dry cask storage by calculating the effects of the destructions of U.S. spent fuel pools following HEMP. Figure 44 is taken from the Air Academy study; it shows dry cask storage could prevent the

---

[339] Op. cit. "Electromagnetic Defense Task Force (EDTF)", p. 13.

radioactive contamination of 94,000 square miles of U.S. land and thus prevent the permanent displacement of more than 3 million Americans (these are conservative figures).

Once spent fuel has remained in the pool long enough to cool enough to permit its removal (radiation and heat levels must be reduced to specific levels), it can be removed from the pool. By November 2020, U.S. nuclear power plants had removed 48% of its spent fuel from spent fuel pools,[340] while about half remained in the pools. Most of the spent fuel removed from the pools was stored in thin-metal canisters (which is put into large metal-lined concrete casks that reduce exposure to radiation and allow passive cooling).

Ten reasons to use thick nuclear waste storage casks

Safety Features	Thin canisters	Thick casks	
1. Thick walls	1/2"- 5/8"	10"- 19.75"	
2. Won't crack		√	
3. Ability to repair, replace seals		√	
4. Ability to inspect (inside & out)		√	
5. Monitor system prevents leaks		√	
6. ASME container certification		√	
7. Defense in depth (redundancy)		√	
8. Store in concrete building		√	
9. Gamma & neutron protection	Need overpack	√	
10. Transportable w/o add'l cask		√	
Market leader	U.S.	World	

SanOnofreSafety.org

Figure 45: Comparison of thin-metal canisters to thick-metal casks for storage of spent nuclear fuel[341]

Unfortunately, the austenitic stainless steels used in thin-metal canisters are known to be susceptible to corrosion and cracking,[342] which

---

[340] Op. cit. "Spent Nuclear Fuel Pools in the U.S.: Reducing the Deadly Risks of Storage"
[341] Gilmore, D. (2023). San Onofre Safety. https://sanonofresafety.org/

can begin internally and is not detectable from outside the canister (inspection is made impossible because the canisters are placed in large metal-lined concrete casks). The internal pressure of the thin-metal canisters cannot be monitored; internal pressure can be monitored with thick-metal casks, which are routinely used outside the U.S. for interim storage.[343] Spent fuel is not retrievable with thin-metal canisters (lids welded on) but is retrievable with thick-metal casks (lids bolted on). Thin-metal canisters were intended for short-term storage and will have to be repackaged,[344] which hopefully will be in the superior thick-metal casks (Figures 45 and 46).

---

[342] "When austenitic stainless steel is welded, the weld metal itself is melted and homogenized. However, with the heat-affected zone (HAZ) near the weld, the steel becomes sensitized. When the metal is heated during the welding process, Cr diffuses from the metal grains into the grain boundaries, where it combines with carbon to form chromium carbides. Sensitization results in the formation of chromium depleted zones at grain boundaries that facilitate the nucleation and propagation of localized corrosion such as pitting (often a precursor for SCC) and SCC [Stress, Cracking, and Corrosion]." Ilgen, A., Bryan, C., Hardin, E. (March 25, 2015). "Draft Geologic Disposal Requirements Basis for STAD Specification", Prepared for U.S. Department of Energy Nuclear Fuels Storage and Transportation Planning Project, Sandia National Laboratories, pp. 29-30. https://www.nrc.gov/docs/ML1613/ML16132A321.pdf

[343] Thin-metal canisters also have to be loaded into metal-lined concrete containers and during the loading process, it is virtually impossible to prevent some contact of the stainless-steel canister with the metal liner, which has the potential to accelerate corrosion and cracking (the concrete containers are necessary to protect workers from radiation emitted by the fuel; concrete containers are not necessary with thick-metal casks which sufficiently block the radiation).

[344] Op. cit. "What Congress Needs to Know About Pending Nuclear Waste Legislation"

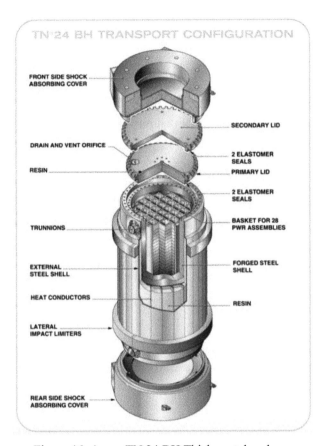

Figure 46: Areva TN 24 BH Thick-metal cask
that holds 69 BWR fuel assemblies for interim
storage[345](there are 74 to 100 fuel rods in each
BWR fuel assembly)

As of 2019, there was $40.9 billion in the Nuclear Waste Fund
(collected from U.S. rate payers), which was meant to finance the
disposal of spent nuclear fuel. However, U.S. Federal law must first be
revised to allow these funds to be used for the removal and storage of
spent fuel from spent fuel pools.[346] Under the Nuclear Waste Policy Act,

[345] Areva TN. (July 2013). "Metal Casks for Used Fuel Transport and Storage".
https://sanonofresafety.files.wordpress.com/2013/06/2013-10-01-2_tn24-a-
rc3a9viser_v7.pdf
[346] The *Nuclear Waste Policy Act* stipulates these funds can only be used for the
permanent disposal of waste. Costs for consolidated interim storage sites are not

the U.S. government cannot accept legal responsibility for spent nuclear fuel until it is received at an open repository site (the funds cannot currently be used for on-site storage). A federal court stopped reactor operator payments to the fund in 2014, because no repository site had been opened (the law required that one be opened by January 31, 1998).

The removal of spent fuel from the pools could also facilitate a move from the high-density storage, now used in the pools, to low-density storage techniques, which the pools were originally designed to use. [347] *"If water were lost from a pool equipped with low-density racks, there would be vigorous, natural convection of air and steam throughout the racks, providing cooling to the spent fuel, which would provide a significant cooling process not currently possible in U.S. spent fuel pools."*[348]

Shield Nuclear Power Plants and Spent Fuel Pools from HEMP

Technology exists that could effectively shield the solid-state electronics and integrated circuits in the Emergency Power Systems and Emergency Core Cooling Systems at U.S. nuclear power plants.

---

borne by the U.S. government, unless title is transferred by amending the *Nuclear Waste Policy Act.*
https://www.eesi.org/briefings/view/111320nuclear An amendment was attempted in 2019 but was not voted on.
https://www.govtrack.us/congress/bills/116/hr2699
[347] Because no long-term storage for spent fuel was opened in the U.S., nuclear utilities were forced to store increasing amounts of spent fuel in their spent fuel pools, which required the use of honeycombed neutron-absorbing storage racks to be placed in the pools. These racks separate the spent fuel and prevent it from restarting nuclear fission (reaching criticality). These racks obviously block the free flow of water through the spent fuel pool.
[348] Thompson, G. (January 31, 2013). "Handbook to Support Assessment of Radiological Risk Arising from Management of Spent Nuclear Fuel", Nautilus Institute for Security and Sustainability, p. 19.
https://nautilus.org/napsnet/napsnet-special-reports/handbook-to-support-assessment-of-radiological-risk-arising-from-management-of-spent-nuclear-fuel/

Retrofitting nuclear power plants to protect them from the massive voltages and currents induced by a HEMP could greatly reduce – and possibly eliminate – the risk of reactor meltdowns, as well as boil-offs in the spent fuel pools. There are experts and technical papers that explain how this can be accomplished.[349] [350] [351]

Because highly radioactive spent fuel must be isolated from the biosphere *for at least 100,000 years*, it is unrealistic to assume it can be monitored for that length of time. There is no current long-term technical solution to high-level nuclear waste storage that is without serious concerns. Proposed geological underground permanent storage solutions have major unresolved technical problems. No nuclear waste containers exist that can withstand the harsh environment that will exist in underground facilities for thousands of centuries.

In 2018, the U.S. Nuclear Waste Technical Review Board stated that:

> *"Long-term research, development, and demonstration of monitoring and sensor technologies are needed to address current technology limitations. . . . direct monitoring of some aspects of overall repository performance is likely not possible over all timescales. For example, some thermal, hydrologic, mechanical, and/or chemical processes that could negatively impact repository performance (e.g., waste package corrosion and breaching, hydrologic resaturation of emplacement drifts,*

[349] International Electrotechnical Commission. (17-May-2017). "Electromagnetic compatibility (EMC) - Part 5-10: Installation and mitigation guidelines - Guidance on the protection of facilities against HEMP and IEMI https://standards.iteh.ai/catalog/standards/iec/b66818ad-403e-47ec-98bb-ba156e7cb367/iec-ts-61000-5-10-2017

[350] Op. cit. Radasky, "Protecting Industry from HEMP and IEMI"

[351] Radasky, W., Savage, E. (Jan 2010). "High-Frequency Protection Concepts for the Electric Power Grid", Metatech Corp, Meta-R-324. https://www.ferc.gov/sites/default/files/2020-05/ferc_meta-r-324.pdf

waste form degradation) may occur only after hundreds to thousands of years. This is much longer than the repository performance confirmation period (100 years during pre-closure for the U.S. program). "[352]

While it appears the long-term solution to storage – geologic underground storage versus storage on the Earth's surface with an almost infinite stewardship (in human terms) – is still a matter of debate, I would argue that conditions on the Earth's surface are far more unstable than those underground. Natural disasters, earthquakes, tsunamis, floods, tornadoes, hurricanes, cyclones, volcanic eruptions, and, of course, terrorism and the possible consequences of a major war between the nuclear weapon states – these all make it unlikely that spent fuel (or nuclear power plants) are likely to escape some catastrophic event in the coming years. It is my opinion that some form of (hardened) underground storage, which utilizes thick-walled metal casks, and which allows for the inspection and retrieval of spent fuel, is the best current option.

Unfortunately, the U.S. Nuclear Regulatory Commission continues to regard nuclear power plants as being immune to the effects of EMP and have declined to validate their assertions through a program of comprehensive testing. Consequently, the citizens of the U.S.A. – as well as those persons residing in nations that have not protected their national electric grid and nuclear power plants[353] – remain very much at risk from the catastrophic effects of HEMP.[354]

---

[352] Nuclear Regulatory Commission. (December 2011). "Resolution of Generic Safety Issues: Issue 20: Effects of Electromagnetic Pulse on Nuclear Power Plants (Rev. 1) (NUREG-0933, Main Report with Supplements 1–35)". https://www.nrc.gov/sr0933/index.html

[353] France could see more than 50 nuclear reactors simultaneously meltdown from a single HEMP.

[354] Op. cit. "Low-Frequency Protection Concepts for the Electric Power Grid".

Postscript

Today, in 2023, there are more than 12,000 nuclear weapons in the arsenals of the nuclear weapon states (the U.S. and Russia own about 90% of them).[355] While the abolition of nuclear weapons would essentially eliminate the danger of HEMP, it appears humanity is unlikely to achieve nuclear abolition in the near future. And since a single nuclear detonation (or a massive Geomagnetic Disturbance) can bring down the U.S. electric power grid – and keep it down for months or a year – it is of the utmost importance that we take action to prevent such a catastrophe by protecting the grid.

Likewise, we must also act to shield our critical national infrastructure – including nuclear power plants – from EMP created by either a nuclear detonation or Intentional Electromagnetic Interference devices.[356] To be clear, I am not a proponent of nuclear power. I don't believe humans should utilize any industrial process that creates massive amounts of toxins that last for centuries or millennia and are lethal at the atomic or molecular level. Although I am proposing safeguards for nuclear power plants, it is because I don't want their reactors to suddenly melt down – I would prefer for them to instead be safely shutdown.

Unfortunately, it does seem unlikely that the U.S. (and the rest of the world) will soon forgo the use of nuclear power. The daily operation of these plants currently increases the U.S. total of highly radioactive

---

[355] Kristensen, H., Korda, M., Johns, E., & Kohn, K. (March 31, 2023). "Status of World Nuclear Forces", Federation of American Scientists. https://fas.org/initiative/status-world-nuclear-forces/

[356] Intentional Electromagnetic Interference (IEMI) devices are not discussed in this book, but they do represent a significant threat to nuclear power plants, see Radasky, W. (October 31, 2018). "Protecting Industry from HEMP and IEMI", In Compliance Magazine. https://incompliancemag.com/article/protecting-industry-from-hemp-and-iemi/

spent fuel by about 2,000 tons a year.[357] Even if all our nuclear power plants were to shut down, there are still more than 85,000 tons of spent fuel now stored on-site at U.S. nuclear power plants[358] (and more than 400,000 tons of spent fuel stored above ground at hundreds of sites around the world[359]).

The best interim solution to isolating spent fuel from the biosphere is to remove most of it from the spent fuel pools (remove the fuel that has been cooling in the pools long enough to be safely exposed to air) and place it in thick-metal casks for monitored storage in hardened underground facilities. I don't believe that this waste can be safely stored for 100,000 years on the Earth's surface because of the many types of natural and man-made disasters that could possibly destroy the containment and release the waste into the environment.

However, the debate about deep underground geologic long-term storage is not yet settled, as the proposed underground geologic storage solutions seem to have major unresolved technical problems.[360] Thus, it appears that a truly safe permanent long-term solution, which will prevent

[357] U.S. Department of Energy. (October 3, 2022). "5 Fast Facts About Spent Fuel", Office of Nuclear Energy. https://www.energy.gov/ne/articles/5-fast-facts-about-spent-nuclear-fuel

[358] Walton, R. (April 1, 2021). "Just the Stats: Volume of U.S. spent nuclear fuel totals 85K metric tons since 1968", Power Engineering. https://www.power-eng.com/nuclear/just-the-stats-volume-of-u-s-spent-nuclear-totals-85k-metric-tons-since-1968/#gref

[359] Le. T. (June 17, 2020). "Spent Nuclear Fuel Storage and Disposal", Nonproliferation. https://www.stimson.org/2020/spent-nuclear-fuel-storage-and-disposal/

[360] In 2018, the U.S. Nuclear Waste Technical Review Board (NWTRB) admitted no country has short-term storage and monitoring technology solutions needed to implement a safe permanent geological repository, stating "Long-term research, development, and demonstration of monitoring and sensor technologies are needed to address *current technology limitations.*" U.S. Nuclear Waste Technical Review Board. (May 2018). "Geologic Repositories: Performance Monitoring and Retrievability of Emplaced High-Level Radioactive Waste and Spent Nuclear Fuel", p. iv. https://www.nwtrb.gov/docs/default-source/reports/nwtrb_perfmonitoring.pdf?sfvrsn=6

this highly radioactive waste from ever getting loose in the biosphere, has yet to be determined. The absolute necessity of keeping these deadly radioactive poisons away from all living things is a problem that will last virtually forever, and if we fail to find a solution, then the result will be a biosphere that will become progressively contaminated with mutagenic, carcinogenic, immunosuppressive radioactive waste.

Appendix 1: Solid State Electronics Susceptible to High Voltage; High-voltage substations; Insulators on Distribution Powerlines

All Figures are in Appendix 1 are from: Savage, Edward, James Gilbert, and William Radasky. (2010). "The Early-Time (E1) High-Altitude Electromagnetic Pulse (HEMP) and Its Impact on the U.S. Power Grid". Metatech Corporation, Meta R-320.
https://www.futurescience.com/emp/ferc_Meta-R-320.pdf

The original Figure and Table numbers are retained with the images.

Figure 6-1. A part (a resistor) exploding under pulse testing, p. 6-1

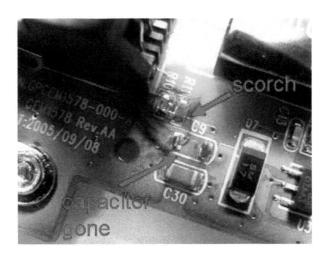

Figure 6-2. Capacitor damage from pulse testing. The capacitor (C9) is gone, and there are scorch marks (C30 shows an undamaged capacitor), p. 6-2

Figure 6-3. The result of pulse testing – IC damage. The IC lid, normally flat, has bubbled, and is discolored from over-heating, p. 6-2

135

Figure 6-7. Arcing at the port to a system. This is computer network card, with the arcing in the connector where the network cable plugs in, p. 6-10

Figure 6-8. Signs of arcing between solder pads on a circuit card, p. 6-10

136

Figure 7-14. The Fisher ROC809 Remote Operations Controller. This is a PLC, such as might be used for remote controlling of a pipeline. It has a computer, and then may be configured with various I/O units: analog, binary, and communications. P. 7-16

Fisher ROC809 unit: Damage was as low as 1 kV for the analog out port, (at 1 kV) the level was too high, and it no longer would work. The Ethernet port was upset at 3 kV, and damaged at 4.5 kV.

Fisher ROC809 Remote Operations Controller					
DUT		Drive	Voltage Level: Charge/Load, kV		
Unit	Port		No Effect	Upset	Damage
ROC809	Discrete In	Differential	-	3.0/3.4	-
	Discrete Out	Differential	-	8.0/5.2	
	Analog In	Differential	8.0/4.5	-	-
	Analog Out	Differential	-	-	1.0/0.6
	Serial Port	Common	-	-	2.5/2.1
	Ethernet	Common	-	3.0/3.0	4.5/4.7
Power Supply	AC In	Differential	8.0/5.1	-	-
Breadth of Effect:		Pulsed Port	Associated Ports		System Wide

Table 7-5. Fast pulse results for the Fisher ROC809 unit, p. 7-17

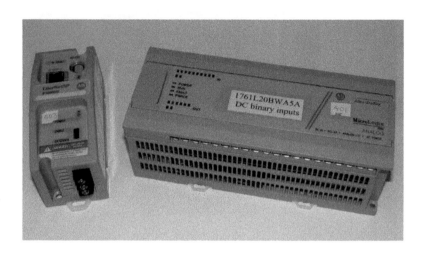

Figure 7-15. The Allen-Bradley MicroLogix 1000 PLC. The PLC, the unit on the right, has analog and binary I/O ports. Its communications is handled by the 1761-NET-ENI unit shown on the left, p. 7-17

Allen-Bradley MicroLogix 1000 PLC					
DUT		Drive	Voltage Level: Charge/Load, kV		
Unit	Port		No Effect	Upset	Damage
MicroLogix 1000 PLC	Discrete In AC	Differential	8.0/7.1	-	-
	Discrete In DC	Differential	-	8.0/6.2	-
		Common	-	4.5/1.6	-
	Discrete Out	Differential	8.0/6.1	-	-
	Analog In, V	Differential	-	-	3.5/3.3
	Analog In, I	Differential	-	2.5/1.7	-
	Analog Out, V	Differential	4.5/2.0	-	-
	Serial Port	Common	-	7.0/5.9	-
	AC power	Differential	8.0/5.0	-	-
ENI	Ethernet	Common	-	4.5/3.9	2*3.5/4.0
Breadth of Effect:		Pulsed Port	Associated Ports		System Wide

Table 7-6. Fast pulse results for the Allen-Bradley MicroLogix 1000 PLC, p. 7-18

138

Allen-Bradley MicroLogix 1000 PLC, CWG Pulse					
DUT		Drive	Voltage Level: Charge/Load, kV		
Unit	Port		No Effect	Upset	Damage
MicroLogix 1000 PLC	Discrete In AC	Differential	-	-	4.0/4.0
	Analog Out, V	Differential	-	-	0.6/0.6
Breadth of Effect:	Pulsed Port		Associated Ports		System Wide

Table 7-7. Slow pulse results for the Allen-Bradley MicroLogix 1000 PLC.(only a few ports were tested), p. 7-18

Compaq PC					
DUT		Drive	Voltage Level: Charge/Load, kV		
Unit	Port		No Effect	Upset	Damage
Network Switch	Downlinks	Common	-	2.5/2.3	-
	Uplink	Common	-	2.0/2.0	-
	AC Power	Differential	8.0/6.8	-	-
PC	LAN PC Card	Common	-	4.5/3.8	-
	Onboard LAN	Common	-	5.0/2.4	-
	Modem	Common	8.0/4.3	-	-
	Serial Port	Common	-	-	0.75/0.5
	AC power	Differential	8.0/5.1	-	-
Breadth of Effect:	Pulsed Port		Associated Ports		System Wide

Table 7-8. Fast pulse results for a typical PC and network switch, p. 7-19

139

E1 HEMP concerns within a high voltage substation

Example of Vertical exposure
of CT leads in conduit on
transformer

Figure 7-18. Exposure of cable conduits on transformers, p. 7-21

The biggest E1 HEMP concern within a high voltage substation is not the high voltage transmission lines and transformers, but rather the low voltage sensor and control lines that extend from the transformer yard to the relays and other control electronics in the control building.

In Figures 7-19 and 7-20 the sensor and control cables are seen to run slightly below ground in trenways that are "buried" in the gravel in the transformer yard. The length of these cables and the poor electromagnetic shielding of the trenway and the gravel at high frequencies will allow the penetration and coupling of high frequency fields to the cables and the subsequent propagation of these currents and voltages to the control building.

140

Figure 7-19. Long runs of "buried" cables in low conductivity gravel, p. 7-22

Figure 7-20. Second view of cable trenway, p. 22

In Figure 7-23 cables extend from the j-boxes to the individual racks of equipment. These cables will carry any remaining high-frequency transients that were coupled to the cables outside, and they will also be coupled to by the electromagnetic fields that propagate through the walls of the building.

Figure 7-23. Distribution of control cables within building to cabinets, p. 7-18

Insulators on Distribution Powerlines

"Approximately 78% of all electric power delivery to end-users is delivered via 15 kV class distribution lines, as highlighted in Table 7-9. . . the likelihood for an optimum exposure of a segment of the line is high, and that at some point along the feeder the maximum E1 HEMP voltage will be induced, creating a possible insulator flashover." p. 7-25

Table 7-9. Summary of the distribution systems for the U.S. power grid, p. 7-26

- Distribution systems in the U.S. o 5,15,25 and 35kV

    o 15kVis77.5%ofallload
    o 35,000 to 40,000 distribution substations
    o Substation size varies from ~1 - 100 MVA with an average of 20 MVA

- Multiple feeders leave the substations
    o 4 to 14 feeders per substation
    o Typically 300 line segments per feeder
    o 60 fault protection and isolation devices per feeder o Average 3 phase feeder length is 10.8 miles
    o 93% of all U.S. feeders are of overhead construction
- End users supplied by feeders o 13.0% industrial load

    o 18.4% supply urban/commercial load o 11.9% rural load
    o 55.7% suburban load

"Prior analysis of the E1 threat by Metatech indicated that induced overvoltages ranging from 200 kV to over 400 kV (depending on the scenario) can occur on these distribution lines over geographically widespread regions, and that if large scale distribution line insulator failure or flashover occurs, the impacted regions will likely experience power grid collapse." p. 7-27

Appendix 2: Emergency Diesel Generator and Battery Bank Schematics

Emergency Diesel Generators

EDGs produce power in a range between 1.5 million watts and 8 million watts (1500 kWe and 8000 kWe).[361]

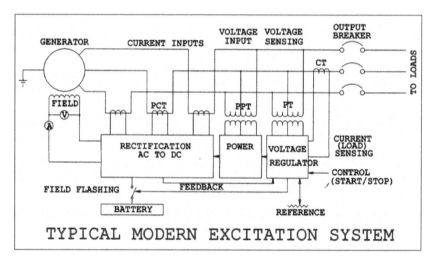

EDG Exciter system (Excitation systems can be defined as the system that provides field current to the rotor winding of a generator.)

Nuclear Regulatory Commission. (January 2011). "Chapter 9, Emergency Diesel Generator, The Generator, Exciter, and Voltage Regulation, Rev 1/11 9-21 of 34 USNRC HRTD, p. 9-30 of 34. https://www.nrc.gov/docs/ML1122/ML11229A143.pdf

---

[361] MTU Onsite Energy, A Rolls-Royce Power Brand System. (2023). "Emergency Diesel Generators for Nuclear Power Plants", p. 4.https://aa-powersystems.com/wp-content/uploads/3061871_OE_Brochure_NPP_2_14_lay_ES.pdf

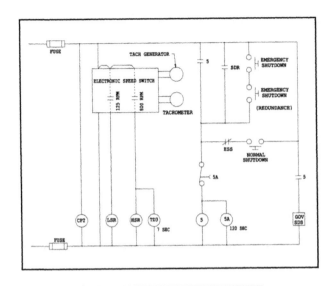

Figure 10-2 Speed Monitoring and Stop Circuitry

Nuclear Regulatory Commission. (January 2011). "Chapter 10, Emergency Diesel Generator EDG Control and Monitoring, Rev 1/11, USNRC HRTD, p. 10-15 of 10-18
https://www.nrc.gov/docs/ML1122/ML11229A158.pdf

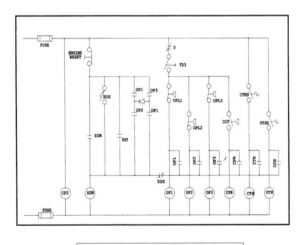

Figure 10-3 Fault Shutdown and Monitoring Circuits

Nuclear Regulatory Commission. (January 2011). "Chapter 10, Emergency Diesel Generator EDG Control and Monitoring, Rev 1/11, USNRC HRTD, p. 10-16 of 18.
https://www.nrc.gov/docs/ML1122/ML11229A158.pdf

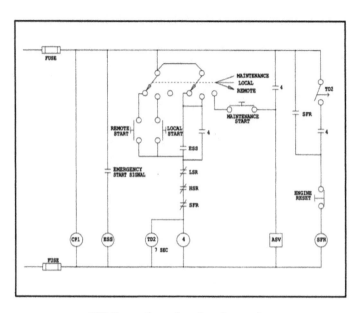

EDG starting circuit schematic

Nuclear Regulatory Commission. (January 2011). "Chapter 10,
Emergency Diesel Generator EDG Control and Monitoring, Rev 1/11,
USNRC HRTD, p. 10-14 of 10-18
https://www.nrc.gov/docs/ML1122/ML11229A158.pdf

Battery Banks

Solid-state components such as rectifiers, inverters, and high-speed switches are susceptible to damage from HEMP E1

Figures 1 and 3 from Clarke, M. (June 2020). "Battery Backups for Nuclear Power Plants", M.E.T.T.S. Ltd, http://www.metts.com.au/battery-backups-for-nuclear-power-plants.html

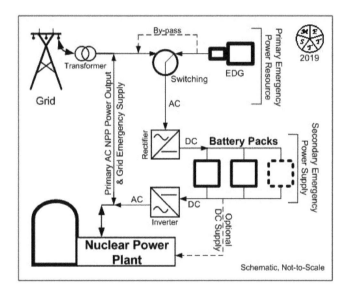

Figure 1. A setup for a battery/EDG power backup system. The batteries can be charged and kept charged either from the grid (usual practice) or from the EDG (during plant testing or emergency grid outages).

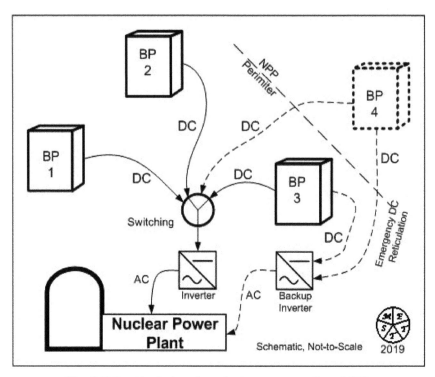

Fig. 3 DC reticulation for a battery storage for a NPP.

The power generated and dispatched by NPPs is high voltage AC; batteries are DC plant. **The two types of plants require power conversion technologies to operate** as part of a generation plant where batteries are used as a backup. **Modern technology for converting DC <--> AC is large-scale electronic solid-state**

Appendix 3: Emergency Core Cooling System Diagrams, Includes location of motor-driven pumps and motor-operated valves

Keys

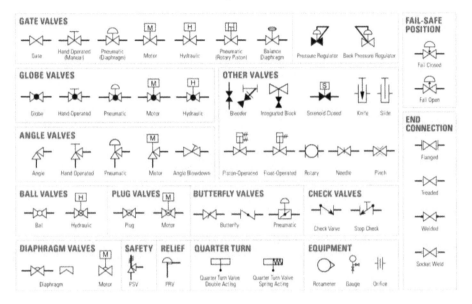

Kimray Inc. (2023). "The Most Common Control Valve Symbols on a P&ID".
https://kimray.com/training/most-common-control-valve-symbols-pid

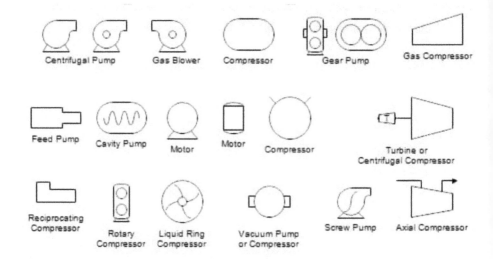

Chemical Tweak. (November 4, 2022). "What is P&ID Uses – P&ID Diagram basics symbols, Pumps and Compresses". https://chemicaltweak.com/p-and-id-diagram-basics/

Boiling Water Reactor (BWR) Diagrams

Source:

Nuclear Regulatory Commission, Reactor Training Branch. (July 2007). "Introduction to Reactor Technology – BWR, Part II, Chapter 10.0, Emergency Core Cooling Systems, pp. 10-10 through 10-13. https://adamswebsearch2.nrc.gov/webSearch2/main.jsp?AccessionNumb er=ML12159A165

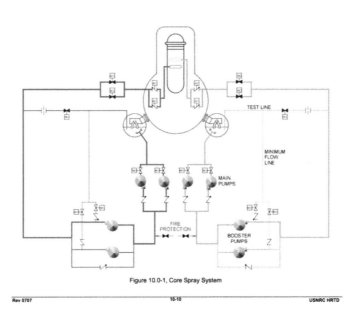

Figure 10.0-1, Core Spray System

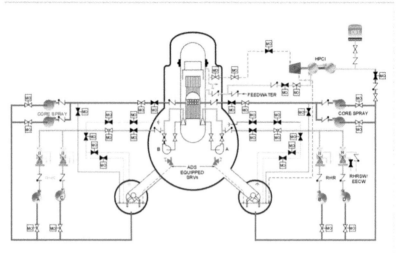

Figure 10.0-2, Typical Emergency Core Cooling System (BWR/3 & BWR/4)

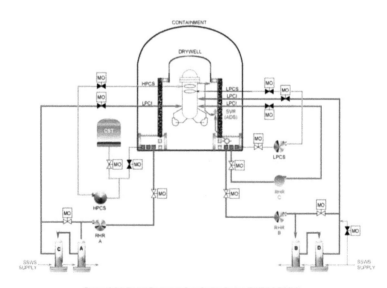

Figure 10.0-3, Typical Emergency Core Cooling System (BWR/5 & BWR/6)

152

Emergency Core Cooling Network

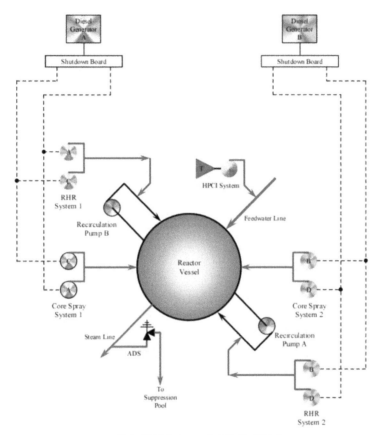

Figure 10.0-4, Emergency Core Cooling Network

153

BWR: Reactor Core Isolation Cooling System

Source:

Nuclear Regulatory Commission, image from

Lochbaum, D. (August 19, 2014), "RCIC Look See", Union of Concerned Scientists, https://blog.ucsusa.org/dlochbaum/rcic-look-see/

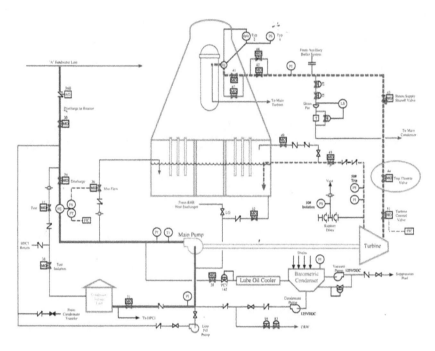

Reactor Core Isolation Cooling System

https://blog.ucsusa.org/wp-content/uploads/2014/07/N36-Figure-1-bwr-ttc-

rcic.jpg?_gl=1*auo36d*_ga*MTg1NDE5NDM2NS4xNjczNTQzNDY1* _ga_VB9DKE4V36*MTY3NTYwODI0Ny4xMy4xLjE2NzU2MDgzMD EuMC4wLjA.

Pressurized Water Reactor (PWR) Diagrams

Source to Key and Diagrams:

> Nuclear Regulatory Commission, Reactor Technology
> Training Branch. (April 2008). "Introduction to
> Reactor Technology – PWR, Part 1, Chapter 1.0
> Introduction to Pressurized Water Reactor Systems",
> Figure 1.0-1, p. 1-14.
> https://www.nrc.gov/docs/ML1215/ML12159A222.pdf

Key

Figure 1.0-1, List of Symbols

155

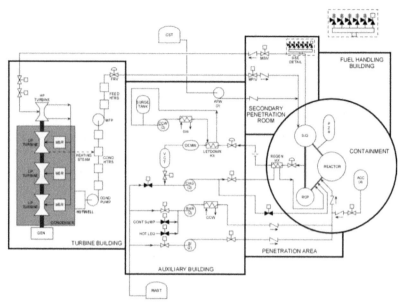

Figure 1.0-2, Plant Systems Composite

156

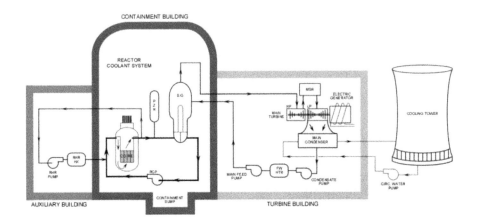

Figure 1.0-4, Basic PWR Arrangement

157

Source for the next two diagrams:

Nuclear Tourist. (N.D.). "Sample ECCS System Drawings".
http://www.nucleartourist.com/systems/eccs.htm

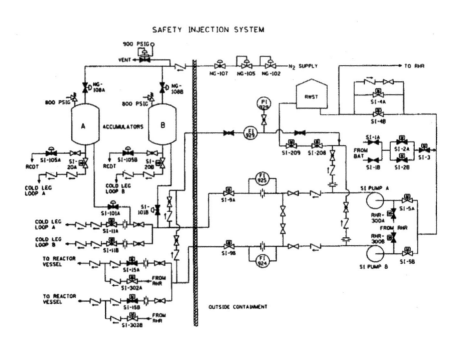

PWR High Head Safety Injection System

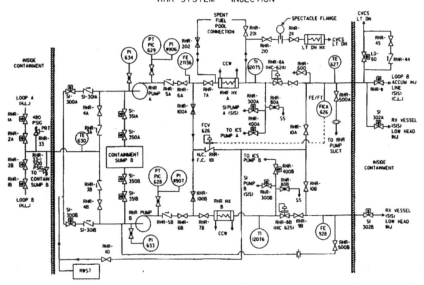

RHR Injection System

Appendix 4: Vulnerability of the National Electric Grid to Geomagnetic Disturbance (GMD)

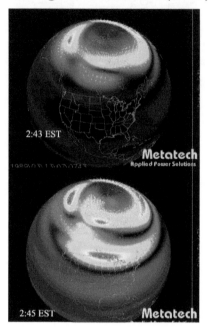 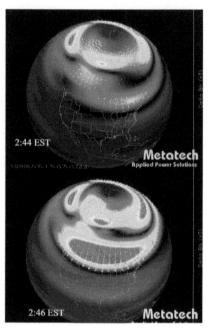

Rapid development of electrojet conditions over North America and principally along U.S./Canada border leads to Hydro Quebec collapse and other reported problems in Minnesota, Manitoba and Ontario at these times. These images depict the ground level geomagnetic intensification for over 4 minutes from 2:43 – 2:46 EST[362]

Research shows that the LPTs and their associated High-Speed Circuit Breakers are highly susceptible to the exceptionally high voltages and currents induced by both HEMP E3 and a massive Geomagnetic Disturbance (GMD); the two phenomena are quite similar in their effects. The U.S. Department of Energy provides this definition of GMD:

---

[362] Kappenman, J. (January 2010). "Geomagnetic Storms and Their Impact on the U.S. Power Grid", Metatech Corporation, Meta-R-319, p. 2-1. https://irp.fas.org/eprint/geomag.pdf

"Geomagnetic disturbances (GMDs) occur when Earth is subjected to changes in the energized particle streams emitted by the Sun. The solar events that cause major GMD events are coronal mass ejections (CMEs), which are eruptions of charged particle plasma from the Sun's corona that can bombard the Earth within as little as 14 hours. Near the Earth's surface, these changes induce currents, known as geomagnetically induced currents (GICs), in long electrical conductor systems such as electric power transmission and distribution lines, communication lines, rail lines, and pipelines. GMDs can have significant negative impacts on the electric grid, including electrical and electronic equipment and systems (e.g., high-frequency radio communications, global navigation satellite systems, long-haul telecommunications/internet exchange carrier lines)." [363]

A massive GMD is thought to occur once every several centuries; the last such event was in the mid-19th century, in 1859, which is called "The Carrington Event", named after the astronomer who first detected the Coronal Mass Ejection that struck the Earth. This GMD lasted several days, with its peak effects exhibited during the first days of September. Telegraph lines melted and failed in the U.S. and Europe, operators in the

[363] U.S. Department of Energy. (January 2019). "Geomagnetic Disturbance Monitoring Approach and Implementation Strategies", p. iv. https://www.energy.gov/ceser/articles/geomagnetic-disturbance-monitoring-approach-and-implementation-strategies

telegraph stations received huge shocks, and sparks flying from the telegraphs ignited fires in the telegraph stations.[364]

Of course, there were no modern electronics in 1859. More recent GMD events have taken place when the Earth was not struck directly by a massive Coronal Mass Ejection. For example, in 1989, when a GMD struck the U.S./Canada border (Figure 3). It took 92 seconds for the power disturbance created by the GMD completely collapse the power grid in Quebec.[365]

It is quite possible that a HEMP *could* occur, but it is an inevitability that another Carrington event *will* occur. And there is no guarantee that another Carrington Event will not occur in the near future. This alone should justify the protection of every national electric grid from GMD – as well as HEMP – since the shielding used for GMD also protects the grid against HEMP.[366]

---

[364] Schwab, J. (May 2023). "Detecting the Perfect Solar Storm", Boston University College of Arts and Sciences.
https://www.bu.edu/cas/magazine/spring12/hughes/

[365] Op. cit. "Geomagnetic Storms and Their Impact on the U.S. Power Grid", p. 2-1.

[366] For detailed information on the effects of Geomagnetic Disturbance on the national electric grid, see Savage, E., Gilbert, J., Radasky. W. (2010). "Geomagnetic Storms and Their Impacts of the U.S. Power Grid", Metatech., Meta R-320. https://www.futurescience.com/emp/ferc_Meta-R-319.pdf and Kappenman, J. (Jan 2010). "Low-Frequency Protection Concepts for the Electric Power Grid: Geomagnetically Induced Current (GIC) and E3 HEMP Mitigation", Metatech Corp, Meta-R-322.
http://www.futurescience.com/emp/ferc_Meta-R-322.pdf

Bibliography

Alvarez, R. Beyea, J. Janberg, K. Kang, J. Lyman, E. Macfarlane, A. Thompson, G. von Hippel, F. (2003). "Reducing the Hazards from Stored Spent Power-Reactor Fuel in the United States", Science and Global Security, 11:1–51. https://scienceandglobalsecurity.org/archive/sgs11alvarez.pdf

Alvarez, R. (May 2011). "Spent Nuclear Fuel Pools in the US: Reducing the Deadly Risks of Storage", Institute for Policy Studies, Washington D.C. https://www.nrc.gov/docs/ML1209/ML120970249.pdf

Alvarez, R. (Winter 2012). "Improving Spent-Fuel Storage at Nuclear Reactors", Issues in Science and Technology, The National Academies of Sciences Engineering Medicine. https://issues.org/alvarez/

America Leadership and Policy Foundation. (June 2015). "Electromagnetic Pulse and Space Weather and the Strategic Threat to America's Nuclear Power Stations: Final Report". https://www.emptaskforce.us/wp-content/pdf/Electromagentic-Pulse-and-Space-Weather-Final-Report-2015.pdf

Areva TN. (July 2013). "Metal Casks for Used Fuel Transport and Storage". https://sanonofresafety.files.wordpress.com/2013/06/2013-10-01-2_tn24-a-rc3a9viser_v7.pdf

Alvarez, R. (June 25, 2013). "Reducing the hazards of high-level radioactive waste in Southern California: Storage of spent nuclear fuel at San Onofre", Friends of the Earth.

https://sanonofresafety.files.wordpress.com/2018/06/songs_spent_fuel_fi
nal-alvarez.pdf

Alvarez, R. (November 13, 2020). "What Congress Needs to Know
About Pending Nuclear Waste Legislation", Environmental and Energy
Study Institute. https://www.eesi.org/briefings/view/111320nuclear

America Leadership and Policy Foundation. (June 2015).
"Electromagnetic Pulse and Space Weather and the Strategic Threat to
America's Nuclear Power Stations: Final Report".
https://www.emptaskforce.us/wp-content/pdf/Electromagentic-Pulse-and-
Space-Weather-Final-Report-2015.pdf

Bays, S., Jayoude, D., Borlodan, G. (April 2019). "Reactor Fundamentals
Handbook, Idaho National Laboratory, INL/EXT-19-53301, p. 56.
https://inldigitallibrary.inl.gov/sites/sti/sti/Sort_13579.pdf
Revision 0 https://inldigitallibrary.inl.gov/sites/sti/sti/Sort_13579.pdf

Behr, P. (Oct 20, 2022), "How a transformer shortage threatens the grid".
E&E News, Energy Wire. https://www.eenews.net/articles/how-a-
transformer-shortage-threatens-the-grid/

Britannica. (2023). "Reactor Control Elements".
https://www.britannica.com/technology/nuclear-reactor/Fuel-
types#ref155173

CIA Factbook, Sting (vectorisation), MTruch (English translation),
Makeemlighter (English translation) -
http://www.lib.utexas.edu/maps/belarus.html, specifically

http://www.lib.utexas.edu/maps/commonwealth/chornobyl_radiation96.jp
g and File:Tchernobyl_radiation_1996.svg for the vector version, CC
BY-SA 2.5. https://commons.wikimedia.org/w/index.php?curid=2628661

Clarke, M. (June 2020). "Battery Backup", Nuclear Engineering
International Magazine.
https://secure.viewer.zmags.com/publication/4d4161a2#/4d4161a2/30

Commission to Assess the Threat to the United States from
Electromagnetic Pulse Attack. (July 2017). "Assessing the Threat from
Electromagnetic Pulse (EMP)Volume I: Executive Report".
https://apps.dtic.mil/sti/pdfs/AD1051492.pdf

Cook, D. Greene, S. Harrington, R. Hodge, S. Yue, D. (1981). "Station
Blackout at Brown's Ferry Unit One – Accident Sequence Analysis",
Oak Ridge National Laboratory, Prepared for the Nuclear Regulatory
Commission. https://www.slideshare.net/srgreene/nuregcr2182vol1

Critical National Infrastructures. (April 2008). "Report of the
Commission to Assess the Threat to the United States from
Electromagnetic Pulse (EMP) Attack".
http://www.empcommission.org/docs/A2473-EMP_Commission-
7MB.pdf

Cybersecurity Division of the Cybersecurity and Infrastructure Security
Agency, National Coordinating Center for Communications, February 5,
2019. "Electromagnetic Pulse (EMP) Protection and Resilience
Guidelines for Critical Infrastructure and Equipment", version 2.2
UNCLASSIFIED.

https://www.cisa.gov/sites/default/files/publications/19_0307_CISA_EMP-Protection-Resilience-Guidelines.pdf

Distributech International, Powergrid International, Dec 21, 2022, "Inaction on electric transformer crisis adds reliability concerns, APPA warns". https://www.power-grid.com/td/inaction-on-electric-transformer-crisis-adds-to-reliability-concerns-appa-warns/#gref

Earthsafe Systems, Inc. (2023). "YQA Generator Day Tanks, 07.12 How much fuel does a generator consume"

Edison Electric Institute, (Jan 2016). "Electromagnetic Pulses (EMPs): Myth vs. Facts". https://inldigitallibrary.inl.gov/sites/STI/STI/INL-EXT-15-35582.pdf

Electric Infrastructure Security Council, "IEMI – Intentional Electromagnetic Interference". https://eiscouncil.org/iemi-intentional-electromagnetic-interference/

Emanuelson, J. (July 7, 2019). "Soviet Test 184: The 1962 Soviet Nuclear EMP Tests Over Kazakhstan". https://www.futurescience.com/emp/test184.html

Ericson, D. et al. (1983). "2 Interaction of Electromagnetic Pulse with Commercial Nuclear Power Plant Systems", Sandia National Laboratories. http://prod.sandia.gov/techlib/access-control.cgi/1982/822738-2.pdf

Foad, B., Abdel-Latif, S., Toshikazu, T. (December 2018). "Reactivity feedback effect on loss of flow accident in PWR", Nuclear Engineering and Technology, Volume 50, Issue 8. https://www.sciencedirect.com/science/article/pii/S1738573317304448

Gauntt, R., Kalinich, D., Cardoni, J., Phillips, J., Goldmann, A., Pickering, S., Francis, M., Robb, K., Ott, L., Wang, D., Smith, C., St.Germain, S., Schwieder, D., Phelan, C. (JULY 2021). "Fukushima Daiichi Accident Study (Status as of April 2012)", Sandia National Laboratories. https://www.osti.gov/servlets/purl/1055601

Gilbert, J., Kappenman, J., Radasky, E., Savage, E. (January 2010), "The Late-Time (E3) High-Altitude Electromagnetic Pulse (HEMP) and Its Impact on the U.S. Power Grid", Metatech Corporation, Meta-R-321. http://www.futurescience.com/emp/ferc_Meta-R-321.pdf

Global Power Supply. (2023). "Power Generation Calculators". https://www.globalpwr.com/power-calculator/

Gonzalez, R., Bible, C. (April 1994). "Application of PLCs for nuclear plant emergency load sequencers", Proceedings of SOUTHEAST CON '94", DOI: 10.1109/SECON.1994.324301 https://ieeexplore.ieee.org/document/324301

Hoerlin, H. (October 1976). "United States High-altitude Test Experiences: A Review Emphasizing the Impact on the Environment", Los Alamos Scientific Laboratory. https://sgp.fas.org/othergov/doe/lanl/docs1/00322994.pdf

Hoffmeister, G. (2017). "Emergency power solutions for nuclear power plants – case studies, considerations, and conclusions", The Institute of Engineering and Technology, Reference Article, doi: 10.1049/etr.2016.0161 ISSN 2056-4007. http://s7d2.scene7.com/is/content/Caterpillar/CM20170217-55802-65351

IAEA Imagebank, CC BY-SA 2.0 <https://creativecommons.org/licenses/by-sa/2.0>, via Wikimedia Commons. https://commons.wikimedia.org/wiki/File:Mike_Weightman_(02810459). jpg

Ilgen, A., Bryan, C., Hardin, E. (March 25, 2015). "Draft Geologic Disposal Requirements Basis for STAD Specification", Prepared for U.S. Department of Energy Nuclear Fuels Storage and Transportation Planning Project, Sandia National Laboratories. https://www.nrc.gov/docs/ML1613/ML16132A321.pdf

Interference Technology. (May 5, 2011). "High Power Electromagnetic (HPEM) Threats to the Smart Grid". https://interferencetechnology.com/high-power-electromagnetic-hpem-threats-to-the-smart-grid/

International Atomic Energy Agency. (2009). "Integrity of Reactor Pressure Vessels in Nuclear Power Plants: Assessment of Irradiation Embrittlement Effects in Reactor Pressure Vessel Steels", IAEA Nuclear Energy Series, No. NP-T-3.1. https://www-pub.iaea.org/MTCD/publications/PDF/Pub1382_web.pdf

International Atomic Energy Agency. (2019). "Passive Safety Systems in Water Cooled Reactors: An Overview and Demonstration with Basic Principle Simulators", Training Course Series 69, Vienna. https://www-pub.iaea.org/MTCD/Publications/PDF/TCS-69web.pdf

International Electrotechnical Commission. (May 17, 2017). "Electromagnetic compatibility (EMC) - Part 5-10: Installation and mitigation guidelines - Guidance on the protection of facilities against HEMP and IEMI https://standards.iteh.ai/catalog/standards/iec/b66818ad-403e-47ec-98bb-ba156e7cb367/iec-ts-61000-5-10-2017

Kadak, A. (June 15, 2012). "Storage of Spent Nuclear Fuel, National Academy of Engineering. https://www.nae.edu/59226/Storage-of-Spent-Nuclear-Fuel

Kappenman, J. (January 2010). "Geomagnetic Storms and Their Impacts of the U.S. Power Grid", Metatech Corporation, Prepared for Sandia National Laboratories. https://www.futurescience.com/emp/ferc_Meta-R-319.pdf

Kappenman, J. (January 2010), "Low-Frequency Protection Concepts for the Electric Power Grid: Geomagnetically Induced Current (GIC) and E3 HEMP Mitigation", Metatech Corporation, Meta-R-322. https://www.ferc.gov/sites/default/files/2020-05/ferc_meta-r-322.pdf

Kellner, T. (October 27, 2021). "Special Power: 'Flexible Transformer' Could Become the Grid's New Superhero". https://www.ge.com/news/reports/special-power-flexible-transformer-could-become-the-grids-new-superhero

Kimray Inc. (2023). "The Most Common Control Valve Symbols on a P&ID". https://kimray.com/training/most-common-control-valve-symbols-pid

Kolev, N. (2009). Multiphase Flow Dynamics 4: Nuclear Thermal Hydraulics, Volume 4. Springer. ISBN 978-3-540-92917-8.

Kozloduy Nuclear Power Plant in Bulgaria., Control Room for Units 3 and 4 (1000 Mwe reactors) they were shut down in 2007. https://commons.wikimedia.org/wiki/File:Kozloduy_Nuclear_Power_Plant_-_Control_Room_of_Units_3_and_4.jpg

Kristensen, H., Korda, M., Johns, E., & Kohn, K. (March 31, 2023). "Status of World Nuclear Forces", Federation of American Scientists. https://fas.org/initiative/status-world-nuclear-forces/

Kuan, P., Hanson, D. J., Odar, F. (1991). "Managing water addition to a degraded core." U.S. Department of Energy Office of Scientific and Technical Information, OSTI 5642843. https://www.osti.gov/servlets/purl/5642843

Kundin, P., "Actuation in Nuclear Power Plants", Valve Magazine, Oct 24, 2011, https://www.valvemagazine.com/articles/actuation-in-nuclear-power-plants

Libmann, J. (1996). Elements of nuclear safety. L'Editeur : EDP Sciences. ISBN 2-86883-286-5

Lochbaum, D. (March 14, 2011). "Reactor Core Cooling".
https://blog.ucsusa.org/dlochbaum/reactor-core-cooling/

Lochbaum, D. (August 19, 2014), "RCIC Look See", Union of
Concerned Scientists,
https://blog.ucsusa.org/dlochbaum/rcic-look-see/

Lochbaum, D. (October 20, 2015). "Nuclear Power(less) Plants", Union
of Concerned Scientists. https://blog.ucsusa.org/dlochbaum/nuclear-
powerless-plants/

Lochbaum, D. (April 5, 2016). "Reactor Core Damage: Meltdown",
Union of Concerned Scientists.
https://blog.ucsusa.org/dlochbaum/reactor-core-damage-meltdown/

Luangdilok, W., Xu, P. (2020). "Chapter 5 – Nuclear plant severe
accidents: challenges and prevention", *Advanced Security and
Safeguarding in the Nuclear Industry*.
https://www.sciencedirect.com/science/article/pii/B97801281825670000
52

Macfarlane, A. (2017). "Risks of Densely Packed Spent Fuel Pools",
Nautilus Institute for Security and Sustainability.
https://nautilus.org/uncategorized/risks-of-densely-packed-spent-fuel-
pools/

Mitsubishi Power Products, Inc. (April 5, 2021). "MEPPI Introduces
245kV Gas Insulated Switchgear for Utility Transmission Applications.

https://meppi.com/news/meppi-introduces-245kv-gas-insulated-switchgear-for-utility-transmission-applications

Mohammed, A. (August 7, 2019). "Circuit Breaker: Learn the Purpose, Cost, and Lead Time to Procure", PEguru: Substation Design & Power System Analysis. https://peguru.com/2019/08/circuit-breaker/#purpose-of-circuit-breaker

M.D'Onorio, A. Maggiacomo, F. Giannetti, G. Caruso. (April 2022). "Analysis of Fukushima Daiichi unit 4 spent fuel pool using MELCOR", Journal of Physics Conference Series, DOI:10.1088/1742-6596/2177/1/012020

MTU Onsite Energy, A Rolls-Royce Power Brand System. (2023). "Emergency Diesel Generators for Nuclear Power Plants", p. 4. https://aa-powersystems.com/wp-content/uploads/3061871_OE_Brochure_NPP_2_14_lay_ES.pdf

Muthukrishnan, V. (April 4, 2021). "SCADA System: What is it?", Electrical 4U. https://www.electrical4u.com/scada-system/

National Coordinating Center for Communications. (Feb 5, 2019). "Electromagnetic Pulse (EMP) Protection and Resilience Guidelines for Critical Infrastructure and Equipment", Version 2.2, National Cybersecurity and Communications Integration Center, Arlington, Virginia.
https://www.cisa.gov/sites/default/files/publications/19_0307_CISA_EMP-Protection-Resilience-Guidelines.pdf

Nuclear Energy Agency, Committee on the Safety of Nuclear Installations. (May 4, 2015). "Status Report on Spent Fuel Pools Under Loss-of-Cooling and Loss-of-Coolant Accident Conditions, Final Report". https://www.oecd-nea.org/jcms/pl_19596/status-report-on-spent-fuel-pools-under-loss-of-cooling-and-loss-of-coolant-accident-conditions-final-report

Nuclear Energy Institute. (Jan 1, 2023). "U.S. Nuclear Plants". https://www.nei.org/resources/us-nuclear-plants
Nuclear Engineering International. (July 20, 2020). "Battery Backup for Nuclear Power Plants". https://www.neimagazine.com/features/featurebattery-backup-for-nuclear-power-plants-8037728/

Nuclear Regulatory Commission. (March 16, 2000). "AP600 Design Control Document, Tier 2 Manual". https://www.nrc.gov/docs/ML0036/ML003691513.pdf

Nuclear Regulatory Commission. (June 2003). "Reactor Concepts Manual: Pressurized Water Reactor Systems", USNRC Technical Training Center. https://www.nrc.gov/reading-rm/basic-ref/students/for-educators/04.pdf

Nuclear Regulatory Commission. (June 2003). "Westinghouse Technology Systems Manual, Section 5.7, Generic Auxiliary Feedwater Systems, USNRC Rev 0603. https://www.nrc.gov/docs/ML1122/ML11223A229.pdf

Nuclear Regulatory Commission. (March 2007). Standard Review Plan, NUREG-0800, 9.5.4. Emergency Diesel Fuel Oil Storage and Transfer System. https://www.nrc.gov/docs/ML0706/ML070680388.pdf

Nuclear Regulatory Commission, Reactor Training Branch. (July 2007). "Introduction to Reactor Technology – BWR, Part II, Chapter 10.0, Emergency Core Cooling Systems. https://adamswebsearch2.nrc.gov/webSearch2/main.jsp?AccessionNumber=ML12159A

Nuclear Regulatory Commission, Reactor Technology Training Branch. (April 2008). "Introduction to Reactor Technology – PWR, Part 1, Chapter 1.0 Introduction to Pressurized Water Reactor Systems". https://www.nrc.gov/docs/ML1215/ML12159A222.pdf

Nuclear Regulatory Commission. (October 2008). "2.2 Reactor Coolant Pumps". https://www.nrc.gov/docs/ML1125/ML11251A015.pdf

Nuclear Regulatory Commission. (October 2008). "Westinghouse Technology Systems Manual; Containment Spray Systems", USNRC Technical Training Center, USNRC HRTD. https://www.nrc.gov/docs/ML1125/ML11251A035.pdf

Nuclear Regulatory Commission. (September 2009). "Westinghouse Technology Systems Manual. Section 3.1, Reactor Vessels and Internals". https://www.nrc.gov/docs/ML1122/ML11223A212.pdf

Nuclear Regulatory Commission. (May 2010). "Theory of Operation of Motor-Operated Valves, Motor-Operated Course Manual, USNRC Technical Training Center. https://www.nrc.gov/docs/ML1134/ML11343A649.pdf

Nuclear Regulatory Commission. (January 2011). "Chapter 10, Emergency Diesel Generator EDG Control and Monitoring, Rev 1/11, USNRC HRTD. https://www.nrc.gov/docs/ML1122/ML11229A158.pdf

Nuclear Regulatory Commission. (January 2011). "Chapter 9, Emergency Diesel Generator, The Generator, Exciter, and Voltage Regulation, Rev 1/11 9-21 of 34 USNRC HRTD. https://www.nrc.gov/docs/ML1122/ML11229A143.pdf

Nuclear Regulatory Commission. (September 29, 2011). "Chapter 1: Diesel Generators as Emergency Power Sources". https://www.nrc.gov/docs/ML1122/ML11229A065.pdf

Nuclear Regulatory Commission. (December 2011). "Resolution of Generic Safety Issues: Issue 20: Effects of Electromagnetic Pulse on Nuclear Power Plants (Rev. 1) (NUREG-0933, Main Report with Supplements 1–35)". https://www.nrc.gov/sr0933/index.html

Nuclear Regulatory Commission. (May 2012). "Diverse and Flexible Strategies (FLEX) Implementation Guide". https://www.nrc.gov/docs/ML1214/ML12143A232.pdf

Nuclear Regulatory Commission, REGULATORY GUIDE 1.137 (July 2012). "Fuel Oil Systems for Emergency Power Supplies". https://www.nrc.gov/docs/ML1230/ML12300A122.pdf

Nuclear Regulatory Commission. (March 9, 2021). "Emergency core cooling systems". https://www.nrc.gov/reading-rm/basic-ref/glossary/emergency-core-cooling-systems-eccs.html

Nuclear Regulatory Commission. (Sept 21, 2022). "Power Reactors". https://www.nrc.gov/reactors/power.html

Nuclear Regulatory Commission. (October 24, 2022). "Reactor Core Isolation Cooling System". https://nrcoe.inl.gov/SysStudy/RCIC.aspx

Nuclear Tourist. (N.D.). "Sample ECCS System Drawings". http://www.nucleartourist.com/systems/eccs.htm

Nuclear Tourist. (Dec 8, 2005). "Emergency Core Cooling Systems". http://www.nucleartourist.com/systems/eccs.htm

Nuclear Tourist. (Dec 8, 2005). "Key Areas and Buildings at the Nuclear Power Plant Site". http://www.nucleartourist.com/areas/areas.htm

Parfomak, P. (June 17, 2014). "Physical Security of the U.S. Power Grid: High-Voltage Transformer Power Stations:", Congressional Research Service, CRS Report Prepared for Members and Committees of Congress.

Peach Bottom Atomic Power Station, Unit 2, Technical Specifications. (N.D.). "Emergency Core Cooling System (ECCS) Instrumentation, B.3.3.5.1.", p. 3.3-98. https://www.nrc.gov/docs/ML0211/ML021190024.pdf

Poloski, J., Grant, G., Gentillion, C., Gaylearn, W., Knudsen, J. (May 1998). "Auxiliary/Feedwater System Reliability, 1987-1995, Idaho National Engineering and Environmental Laboratory, NUREG/CR-5500, INEEL/EXT-97-00740, Vol. 1. https://nrcoe.inl.gov/publicdocs/SystemStudies/nureg-cr-5500-vol-1.pdf

Postelwait, J. (July 12, 2022). "Transformative Times: Update on the US.S. Transformer Supply Chain", T&D World. https://www.tdworld.com/utility-business/article/21243198/transformative-times-update-on-the-us-transformer-supply-chain

QuantiServ. (January 26, 2021). https://www.quantiserv.com/2021/01/26/nuclear-power-plant-emergency-generator-engine-block-repair/

Radasky, W., Savage, E. (Jan 2010). "High-Frequency Protection Concepts for the Electric Power Grid", Metatech Corp, Meta-R-324. https://www.ferc.gov/sites/default/files/2020-05/ferc_meta-r-324.pdf

Radasky, W., Pry, P. (July 6, 2010). "Rebuttal to "The EMP threat: fact, fiction, and response", The Space Review in association with Space News. https://www.thespacereview.com/article/1656/1

Radasky, W., Savage, E. (Jan 2010). "High-Frequency Protection Concepts for the Electric Power Grid", Metatech Corp, Meta-R-324. https://www.ferc.gov/sites/default/files/2020-05/ferc_meta-r-324.pdf

Radasky, W., Savage, E. (Jan 2010). "Intentional Electromagnetic Interference (IEMI) and Its Impact on the U.S. Power Grid ", Metatech Corp, Meta-R-323. https://www.futurescience.com/emp/ferc_Meta-R-323.pdf

Radasky, W. (October 31, 2018). "Protecting Industry from HEMP and IEMI", In Compliance Magazine. https://incompliancemag.com/article/protecting-industry-from-hemp-and-iemi/

Report of the Commission to Assess the Threat to the United States from Electromagnetic Pulse (EMP) Attack. (April 2008). "Critical National Infrastructures". http://www.empcommission.org/docs/A2473-EMP_Commission-7MB.pdf

Rust, J., Weaver, L. (1976). *Nuclear Power Safety*, General Features of Emergency Core Cooling Systems. https://www.sciencedirect.com/topics/engineering/core-cooling

Savage, E., Gilbert, J., Radasky, W. (January 2010). "The Early-Time (E1) High-Altitude Electromagnetic Pulse (HEMP) and Its Impact on the U.S. Power Grid", Metatech Corporation, Meta-R-320. http://www.futurescience.com/emp/ferc_Meta-R-320.pdf

Schwab, J. (May 2023). "Detecting the Perfect Solar Storm", Boston University College of Arts and Sciences. https://www.bu.edu/cas/magazine/spring12/hughes/

Secure the Grid Coalition, (Jan 12, 2023). "EMP: Technology's Worst Nightmare". https://securethegrid.com/emp-technologys-worst-nightmare/

State of Nevada. (2023). "The Fight Against Yucca Mountain". https://ag.nv.gov/Hot_Topics/Issue/Yucca/

Statement of David Lochbaum, Director, Nuclear Safety Project, Before the Senate Committee on Energy and Natural Resources. (July 20, 2013). https://www.energy.senate.gov/services/files/89dbc888-171c-4f77-8ecf-83a0055fcfb9

Steinkamp, H. (1995). "Emergency Venting of Pressure Vessels", International Atomic Energy Association, International Information System. https://inis.iaea.org/collection/NCLCollectionStore/_Public/28/005/28005402.pdf

Stuckenberg, D., Woolsey, J., DeMaio, D. (November 2018). "Electromagnetic Defense Task Force (EDTF)", Air University Press Maxwell Air Force Base, Alabama, LeMay Paper No. 2. https://www.airuniversity.af.edu/Portals/10/AUPress/Papers/LP_0002_DeMaio_Electromagnetic_Defense_Task_Force.pdf

Stuckenberg, D., Woolsey, J., DeMaio, D. (August 2019). "Electromagnetic Defense Task Force (EDTF) Report 2.0, LeMay Paper No. 4", Air University Press, Maxwell Air Force Base, Alabama, Appendix 1.
https://www.airuniversity.af.edu/Portals/10/AUPress/Papers/LP_0002_D eMaio_Electromagnetic_Defense_Task_Force.pdf

Suharno, I. (2007) "Core Cooling Mechanism on Loss of Flow Accident of PWR Power Reactor", International Atomic Energy Association, International Information System.
https://inis.iaea.org/search/search.aspx?orig_q=RN:45006338

The Douglas Company. Retrieved May 2023 from
https://www.douglascompany.com/tag/electrical-components/

The Foundation for Resilient Societies, "Estimating the Cost of Protecting the US Electric Grid from Electromagnetic Pulse, September 2020.
https://www.resilientsocieties.org/uploads/5/4/0/0/54008795/estimating_t he_cost_of_protecting_the_u.s._electric_grid_from_electromagnetic_puls e.pdf

Thompson, G. (January 31, 2013). "Handbook to Support Assessment of Radiological Risk Arising from Management of Spent Nuclear Fuel", Nautilus Institute for Security and Sustainability, p. 19.
https://nautilus.org/napsnet/napsnet-special-reports/handbook-to-support-assessment-of-radiological-risk-arising-from-management-of-spent-nuclear-fuel/

Union of Concerned Scientists, "Nuclear Power(less) Plants", October 2015, https://allthingsnuclear.org/dlochbaum/nuclear-powerless-plants

U.S.-Canada Power System Outage Task Force. (April 2004). "U.S.-Canada Power System Outage Task Force, Final Report on the August 14, 2003 Blackout in the United States and Canada: Causes and Recommendations". https://www.energy.gov/sites/default/files/oeprod/DocumentsandMedia/BlackoutFinal-Web.pdf

U.S. Department of Commerce. (October 15, 2020). "The Effect of Imports of Transformers and Transformer Components on the National Security, Final Report", Bureau of Industry and Security , Office of Technology Evaluation. https://www.bis.doc.gov/index.php/documents/section-232-investigations/2790-redacted-goes-report-20210723-ab-redacted/file

U.S. Department of Energy. (June 1992). "DOE Fundamentals Handbook: Thermodynamics, Heat Transfer, and Fluid Flow," DOE-HDBK-1012/2-92. https://engineeringlibrary.org/reference/heat-transfer-decay-heat-doe-handbook

U.S. Department of Energy. (March 2017). "Strategic Transformer Reserve", Report to Congress. https://www.energy.gov/sites/prod/files/2017/04/f34/Strategic%20Transformer%20Reserve%20Report%20-%20FINAL.pdf

U.S. Department of Energy. (January 2019). "Geomagnetic Disturbance Monitoring Approach and Implementation Strategies".

https://www.energy.gov/ceser/articles/geomagnetic-disturbance-monitoring-approach-and-implementation-strategies

U.S. Department of Energy, Office of Electricity Delivery and Energy Reliability. (April 2014). "Large Power Transformers and the U.S. Electric Grid". https://www.energy.gov/sites/prod/files/2014/04/f15/LPTStudyUpdate-040914.pdf

U.S. Department of Energy, Office of Electricity. "Addressing Security and Reliability Concerns of Large Power Transformers". Retrieved June 1, 2023, from https://www.energy.gov/oe/addressing-security-and-reliability-concerns-large-power-transformers

U.S Department of Energy, Office of Nuclear Energy. (August 2020). "Integration of FLEX Equipment and Operator Actions in Plant Force-=On-Force Models With Dynamic Risk Assessment, Light Water Reactor Sustainability Program". https://lwrs.inl.gov/Physical%20Security/Integration_FLEX_Equipment_Operator_Actions.pdf

U.S. Department of Energy, Infrastructure Security and Energy Restoration Office of Electricity Delivery and Energy Reliability (April 2014) "Large Power Transformers and the US Electric Grid", p. vi. https://www.energy.gov/sites/prod/files/2014/04/f15/LPTStudyUpdate-040914.pdf

U.S. Energy Information Administration. (July 13, 2022). "Nuclear Explained: Nuclear Power Plants".

https://www.eia.gov/energyexplained/nuclear/nuclear-power-plants-types-of-reactors.php

United States Dept of Homeland Sec. (2007), National Preparedness Guidelines.
http://www.fema.gov/pdf/emergency/nrf/National_Preparedness_Guidelines.pdf

USNRC Technical Training Center, Reactor Concepts Manual. (June 2003). "Reactor Concepts Manual Pressurized Water Reactor Systems".
https://www.nrc.gov/docs/ML2005/ML20057E160.pdf

USNRC Technical Training Center, Reactor Concepts Manual, (June 2003). "Reactor Concepts Manual Pressurized Water Reactor Systems".
https://www.nrc.gov/reading-rm/basic-ref/students/for-educators/04.pdf

Vaschenko, A. (November 1, 2006). "Russia: Nuclear Response to America Is Possible Using Super-EMP Factor", "A Nuclear Response To America Is Possible," Zavtra,

Vaschenko, A., Belous, V. (April 13, 2007); "Preparing for the Second Coming of 'Star Wars", *Nezavisimoye Voyennoye Obozreniye* translated in *Russian Considers Missile Defense Response Options* CEP20070413330003.

Walsh, E. (April 8, 1977). "Carter Acts to Curb the Spread of Plutonium", The Washington Post.
https://www.washingtonpost.com/archive/politics/1977/04/08/carter-acts-to-curb-spread-of-plutonium/ef0ef035-b6e6-4b90-94e3-c3109d2692eb/

Walton, R. (April 1, 2021). "Just the Stats: Volume of U.S. spent nuclear fuel totals 85K metric tons since 1968", Power Engineering. https://www.power-eng.com/nuclear/just-the-stats-volume-of-u-s-spent-nuclear-totals-85k-metric-tons-since-1968/#gref

Widodo, S., Ekariansyah, A., Tjahjono, H. (August 2016). "AP1000 Partial and Complete Loss of Flow Accidents Analysis Using RELAP5", National Technology Nuclear Seminar 2016, ISSN: 2355-7524. https://digilib.batan.go.id/e-prosiding/File%20Prosiding/Iptek%20Nuklir/SENTEN_2016/DATA/681_Surip%20Widodo.pdf

World Nuclear Association. (May 2022). "Fukushima Daiichi Accident". https://world-nuclear.org/information-library/safety-and-security/safety-of-plants/fukushima-daiichi-accident.aspx

Wright, D. (March 27, 2011). Where Did the Water in the Spent Fuel Pools Go?", Union of Concerned Scientists. https://allthingsnuclear.org/dwright/where-did-the-water-in-the-spent-fuel-pools-go/

Zhao Meng, Da Xinyu, and Zhang Yapu, (May 1, 2014). "Overview of Electromagnetic Pulse Weapons and Protection Techniques Against Them" Winged Missiles (PRC Air Force Engineering University.

Zhegang, M. Kellie, K. Schoeder, J. Wierman, T. (December 2019). "Safety Study: High Pressure Safety injection 1998-2018", Idaho

National Laboratory, Department of Energy National Laboratory. https://inldigitallibrary.inl.gov/sites/sti/sti/Sort_21672.pdf

Acknowledgements

Many thanks to Dr. William Radasky of the Metatech Corporation for allowing me to use the figures, images, and data taken from the Metatech publications. Dr. Radasky kindly attempted to educate me about the nature of EMP and HEMP. He is not responsible for any errors I may have made in this report; the conclusions I reach in this report are entirely my own.

Thanks to Ammad Zulfiqar for designing the front cover (ammadzulfi@gmail.com).

I also would like to thank other individuals who assisted me and patiently answered my questions about nuclear power plants, including Arnie Gundersen, Dr. M.V. Ramana, Professor Dr. Tatsujiro Suzuki, Dr. Tillman Ruff.

Many thanks to Dr. David Stuckenberg, who was the lead author of the studies done by the U.S. Air Force Air University Electromagnetic Defense Task Force. Dr. Stuckenberg provided me with important information about how the U.S. Air Force uses software to model, plan for, and defend against the effects of nuclear high-altitude electromagnetic pulse.

Thanks also go to my good friends Greg Mello, Trisha Mello, and Dr. James Marzolf, for all their support, encouragement, and advice.

Dr. Alan Phillips was a great mentor and friend to me. Both Alan and his wonderful wife, Joy, supported my work for years and it was because of their assistance that I was able to write, as well as travel around the world and speak on nuclear weapon issues. I would not have taken this path had it not been for Alan.

A great debt of gratitude is owed to my dear sister, Dr. Sydney Starr, whose kindness probably saved my life, and to whom I want to dedicate this book.

Finally, I wish to keep a promise and also dedicate this book to Casey Yocks, who inspired me to travel to New York and speak at a 2019 U.N. side panel, an event that caused me to focus on HEMP.

Milton Keynes UK
Ingram Content Group UK Ltd.
UKHW021953281024
450365UK00013B/688

9 788793 987357